Studying Science at U

Studying Science at University

Everything you need to know

Clare Rhoden and
Robyn Starkey

ALLEN & UNWIN

First published in 1998 by
Allen & Unwin
9 Atchison Street
St Leonards NSW 2065
Australia
Phone: (61 2) 9901 4088
Fax: (61 2) 9906 2218
E-mail: frontdesk@allen-unwin.com.au
Web: http://www.allen-unwin.com.au

National Library of Australia
Cataloguing-in-Publication entry:

Rhoden, Clare, 1955– .
   Studying science at university: everything you need to
   know.

   ISBN 1 86448 518 3.

   1. Science—Study and teaching (Higher). 2. Study skills.
   I. Starkey, Robyn, 1965– . II. Title.

507.11

Set in 10.5/13 Garamond Book by Bookhouse Digital, Sydney
Printed and bound by Southwood Press, Sydney

10 9 8 7 6 5 4 3 2 1

FOREWORD

When the euphoria of being accepted into university has worn off, many students are unpleasantly surprised to find that studying at university isn't at all what they expected. *Studying Science at University* focuses on the skills that will help Science students adapt to the changed learning environment that university study presents. The authors, Clare Rhoden and Robyn Starkey, are both academic skills advisers at the University of Melbourne's Learning Skills Unit and their approach is firmly grounded in the experience of listening to the concerns of many young students.

Most students want to do as well as they can, completing their degree in the minimum time; the authors provide solutions and strategies that help avoid the pitfalls, but at the same time they introduce techniques that develop learning skills and organisational strategies that students will take with them into the workforce.

Patricia McLean
Manager, Equity and Learning Programs
University of Melbourne

CONTENTS

LIST OF TABLES AND FIGURES

Tables

Figures

ACKNOWLEDGMENTS

We would like to thank a number of people who helped us with this project: Dr Bruce Grant, for his comments and advice; Peter Akatow; and our colleagues at the Learning Skills Unit, particularly Aveline Pérez. We would also like to express our appreciation to Fiona Benson, Bennett Foddy and all the other students at Melbourne University whose experiences are the basis for a lot of the information in this book.

INTRODUCTION

HOW THIS BOOK WORKS

What is this book going to do for me?

Studying science at tertiary level is a challenging task. Some students are dismayed to discover that their classes are so different from the science classes they attended at secondary school. In this chapter we'll look at some of the differences that exist and the reasons for those differences. Understanding the way your learning environment has changed when you get to university is an important first step towards successful tertiary study.

Often, students who are offered a place in a science course at university are very high achievers, and yet they find that the study strategies that have been so successful for them at secondary level do not gain equivalent results at tertiary standard. The purpose of this book is to introduce you to the ways in which science is studied in post-secondary settings, and to help you avoid the disappointment of poor results by showing you some effective study strategies for university level.

Meet our sample science students . . .

Science students have a fair bit in common, but every student who does a science degree does something a little different. In this book, we have chosen three students to provide examples of different study situations and problems. We hope that between them, they cover a wide range of the sorts of experiences that you might have as a first year science student. Sometimes it helps to hear about other students' problems and solutions.

To help us understand how studying at university is different from school—and the best ways of coping with those differences—we'll hear from them about their experiences, and watch as they approach and then complete their first year at university.

Zoe is studying a specific set of subjects as she is trying to get into veterinary science next year. This means that she has selected a more structured course with probably a smaller number of fellow students all doing the same subjects.

Sam is doing a general science degree—a BSc— because he likes science and was good at it at school. However, he has no real notion of what career he would like and is unfocused about his subject courses. He is living in college, so he is getting to know lots of people there. Because his science classes are very big, he hasn't really talked to anyone who isn't also at college.

Joel is doing a combined arts/science degree because he likes science but he enjoys working with people and he has an idea that perhaps he'll one day be a great psychologist. He's doing biology, sociology, psychology and the history and philosophy of science. He comes from a state high school and has few friends at the uni.

LEARNING TO BE A UNI STUDENT

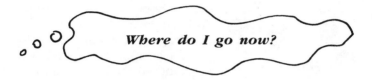

Where do I go now?

CLASS FORMAT

The first big change that you will notice is that science classes are different at tertiary level. For example, if you have come from a secondary school where the classes in final year science had fewer than twenty students, your class sizes will obviously be much larger. At many tertiary institutions, first year science courses will consist of 2–3 lectures a week of up to 400 students, and one laboratory or practical session with 60 or more students in the class. This means that you can expect very little in the way of individual attention. Most first year science students will have 20–25 hours of lectures, pracs (practical laboratory sessions), and tutes (tutorials) every week.

Lectures form the basis of your study at university. In two or three lectures a week, you will be introduced to the theoretical side of the course. During a first year lecture, students take notes, and are not usually expected to ask or answer questions during the lecture. If you would like to ask something, most lecturers are happy to talk to you. Try just before or just after class.

What happens in lectures?

Unlike classes at secondary school, lectures will not provide you with all the information you are expected to become familiar with—even with three hours of lectures a week, you are still expected to read from your textbooks and other sources (printed lecture notes, reading packs, and academic journals, for example) to cover each topic in sufficient depth.

What's the difference between a lecture and a tutorial?

In addition to lectures, you will have either tutorials or practical classes—or both! In the tutorials, you will be with a smaller group of students and the tutor will take you through various problems that have been set, or perhaps just show you how to start solving the problems on your own. Often the tute class will not complete the whole sheet of problems, and you will need to do these yourself. Tutes do give you the chance to speak up and ask questions. Get to know your tutors—they're the first people you should go to if you are unsure about course material or assessment.

What do I do in a "lab"?

You will also have practical or 'laboratory' classes most weeks. These are generally two to three hours long and in them you will work with a small group of fellow students on experiments that relate to the lecture material. You will have about four other people to work with, but the whole lab or prac class may have 50 to 100 students in it. There will be three or four 'demonstrators' or tutors who will show you how to go about performing the experiment and help you if you run into problems. Like tutors, demonstrators can be very helpful and they are the ones you can most easily develop a good working relationship with.

Lecturers will talk to students and do their best to be available to answer questions, but because there are so many students, it is difficult for individual students to relate to the lecturer easily. In the pracs you will learn various experimental procedures or techniques which may be assessed at the end of semester. You will also have a prac report to write either during the prac class itself or in the following week, and don't be shocked if you sometimes need to stay back to complete an experiment that is going slowly. You will be expected to do quite a bit of work on your own.

FITTING IN TO THE UNIVERSITY 'COMMUNITY'

One consequence of these teaching methods is that students can feel isolated, as it can be difficult to get to know people in classes of such a large size. Not only is it impossible for the teachers—lecturers, demonstrators and tutors—to know everyone in the class, it is also difficult at first for you to recognise more than a few fellow students. Many university students make friends on the very first day with the person who happens to sit next to them at the first lecture they attend.

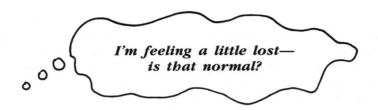

*I'm feeling a little lost—
is that normal?*

Often students feel that 'everyone else seems to have friends/know where they are going/know what to do', but usually this is an illusion. Most of the first years are equally shy and lost in their early weeks at university. A few students have friends from their high school in the same tertiary course, but this is the exception rather than the rule.

> Zoe says: 'My older sister knew quite a few people from school when she started uni; and she hung around with them a lot in her first semester. After a while she met new people she liked more. She says that students who are forced to meet new people because they don't know anyone are lucky. I'm not sure I agree. I want to keep in touch with my school friends.'

Many universities run special functions in Orientation Week (the week before first semester starts) to help students overcome these problems, and some faculties and departments run specific schemes to help incoming students adjust to their new learning environment. University student unions have lots of clubs and societies that you can join. These cater for a range of interests from singing to skiing to science. It's a very good idea to attend some of these events and join one or two of these schemes and/or groups so that you can quickly find some friendly fellow students, find your way around, and then get on with the serious business of studying and enjoying university life.

Another consequence of attending large classes is that you are more responsible for your own learning. The lecturers see so many students over the course of each week that they can't be expected to remember individual first year students, and the lecturers, tutors and demonstrators are responsible for their own research as well as classes. It isn't part of their job to chase after you and make sure you are keeping up with your studies.

Taking the responsi-bull by the horns!

It's up to you to organise your own study regime and to keep up with the material. In fact, the sooner you can convince yourself to start, the better you will cope. New students often find this expectation—that they take responsibility themselves for their work—a great change from schooldays. This can be a liberating concept. However, it may be difficult to adjust, especially if you tend to procrastinate about study.

How can I keep up?

PACE OF MATERIAL

At tertiary level, topics are covered at a faster rate than at school. Two or three lectures in one week may be equal to half a term's work at secondary school. If you don't realise just how much material is covered in each lecture, you won't allow enough time to prepare for the examinations at the end of semester. To get this into perspective, you should take into account that the university teaching year is 26–28 weeks long, and yet you will cover up to four times the amount of material that you learned at school in 35–39 weeks each year.

So you can't leave all your revision until 'swot vac' (the time between the end of classes and the start of exams; probably a week, sometimes two): there just won't be enough time in those few days to read over all the material in the semester's curriculum, let alone study the ideas properly and practise answering questions. You need to work steadily throughout the semester to develop a good overview of the course.

I think I've heard all this before!

You probably have been given this sort of advice before, and ignored it. However, because of the weighting of assessment in science courses (80–100 per cent on the end of semester exam), this notion of constant revision and steady work is more important than ever before. We'll talk about the assessment procedures and what they mean later in this book—Chapters 8 and 9 look at written assessment tasks, and Chapters 10 and 11 are all about exams. Just remember that if you don't understand something, it's no use waiting until the end of the course to ask someone to explain it to you—you'll be too far behind. (If you need to ask a question, do it straight away, in your next class.) There are strategies to employ which can help you around these difficulties, and we'll discuss them throughout this book.

However, don't think that your life at university needs to be one long, long slog where you have your head down over your desk for sixteen uninterrupted weeks each semester—far from it! You can really do quite well by working steadily—not necessarily night and day, but doing some study often—over the weeks, completing a certain amount of all your tasks. The curriculum is so large that you can still do very well even though you don't know everything perfectly.

'THESE STUDENTS DON'T KNOW ANYTHING!' VERSUS 'THEY NEVER GIVE US PROPER EXPLANATIONS!'

Sometimes university teaching staff feel disappointed with the knowledge level of the students admitted to their courses. You may have seen reports criticising current secondary schooling and assessment procedures. Some university staff would be happier to set their own entrance examinations in order to screen the students themselves. Lecturers have expressed this as 'They know all about dolphins and trawling, and surfing the internet, but they don't know their periodic tables!'

The truth of the matter is that today's successful school leaver may be a very different person from the university entrant of twenty years ago. Today's universities have a larger variety of students than ever before. For instance, a greater proportion of students now complete six years of secondary education and so become eligible to be considered for university entrance. These students are from a more diverse range of backgrounds than formerly. They have a wider range of skills and interests than the 'academically inclined' successful matriculant of the 1960s and 1970s. Only recently has the university community begun to appreciate how such diversity can be a positive force in tertiary pursuits.

Universities in general expect a great deal of their students, and this is reflected in the attitudes of the teaching staff. This mismatch between what lecturers expect you to know and what you actually bring with you from secondary school can cause problems. Complacency can be a big trap, especially for students who did well in Year 12 (that is, in their final year of secondary schooling). You are expected to come to university with an enquiring mind, to have the initiative and interest to follow up topics that interest you, and to go about your own work without needing to be spoon-fed.

Lecturers, tutors and demonstrators believe that successful students will want to understand the concepts and will therefore have no difficulty in doing so. If you are enthusiastic about what you learn, of course this will help to keep you motivated, and that's important. But something that is equally important is the ability to keep an open mind and be willing to adapt. Tertiary teachers are not the same as secondary teachers; they often won't tell students exactly what to do. Instead, they expect you to learn by following their example, or by applying a rule or theory to a new situation.

Even students who did brilliantly in Year 12 will have to make many adjustments.

You'll be going through lots of changes. There are rapid advances being made in all fields of science and technology, so the gap between secondary science and tertiary science can be huge. For example, first year biological science students are introduced to more new vocabulary than arts students who go from studying a foreign language in Year 12 to studying that language at first year university level. This means that no matter how much they want to understand the new concepts, first year science students can find their courses very difficult.

> Joel says: 'I'm really interested in genetics. We studied it a bit in Year 12 Biology, and I'd like to do more. I looked up the genetics subjects for second year to see what I could do, and I didn't even understand the handbook. Will I really learn that much in a year?'

On the other hand, all the new information can be a challenge which fascinates and inspires you to discover more and more yourself. You have assets to offer the tertiary education sector which have never been seen there before—because you've never been there before—and it may be your contribution to science that changes the way we look at theories and practices.

LACK OF FEEDBACK

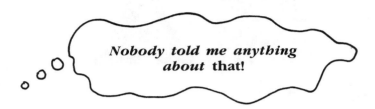

Nobody told me anything about **that!**

Large class sizes, teaching staff with other responsibilities, and little direction about how to organise your study may make it difficult for you to judge how well you are going. University students are notorious for under- or over-reporting the amount of study they do, so you can't always rely on the estimates of friends and acquaintances for comparison with your own performance. The absence of continuous assessment procedures means that you may not know if you're doing enough work.

How much study is enough—can anybody tell you?

Students commonly have unrealistic expectations of how much material they can cover during swot vac. If you decide to spend all your time joining clubs and making friends, you won't be the only one, but will you be a successful student?

There certainly is a place for socialisation in a well-balanced timetable, but the important concept here is *balance.* Leaving all your study tasks until the last minute may make you work very quickly at the end of the semester (when you are in a flat panic), but because you receive so much information throughout the semester, you can't possibly cover everything in a short space of time (no matter how many cups of coffee you have).

ASSESSMENT

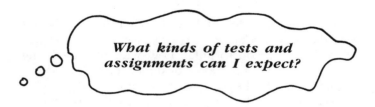

What kinds of tests and assignments can I expect?

Many science courses at tertiary level are assessed wholly by the end of semester exam. For a great number of students, these will be the first 100 per cent assessment exams they have ever sat, and perhaps the first time they have sat a three-hour exam. Facing a long exam in a very large room with hundreds of other more-or-less frightened students around you can be daunting. Some science exams will have short or longer essay-style answers, some will require you to solve problems, and some will have a multiple choice component. In addition, many courses will assess your practical work either on your weekly performance and written prac reports, or in a special practical examination.

PERFORMANCE

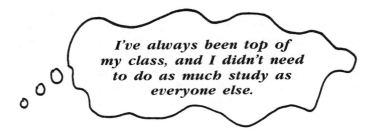

I've always been top of my class, and I didn't need to do as much study as everyone else.

Most science courses have very little in the way of assignments, but a few will require you to hand in one or two small tasks such as problems or reports. For some students, the shock of failing or doing badly on one of these small tasks is great—these are students who previously may never have failed a single assessment. At university, of course, the standards are higher because everyone in the course obtained at least the entrance level mark. In fact, you can think of it as everyone else in the room being as smart or smarter than you are. Some students come in expecting to be a star because they were always in the top 10 per cent at their high school, but you need to get these things into perspective. A class comprised entirely of the top students from secondary school is likely to perform at a higher level than your old secondary school class in the same subject; by comparison, you may perform at a lower level than you are accustomed to.

Only when you have failed or performed poorly in one or more of your subjects are you alerted to the fact that study at tertiary level requires a different approach. At the very worst, you'll have to repeat some subject(s). Most universities and courses recognise that first year is a time of adjustment. There are lots of ways to get help—we'll talk about a few of them later in this book. Failing a subject at university can be crushing, but it isn't like failing in Year 12, when it meant not getting into university. You'll be given lots of opportunities to repair your mistakes.

How this book can help you to adapt

Of course, prevention is better than cure, and there are very good ways to prepare for tertiary assessment tasks. In the following chapters you will find practical suggestions for keeping up with the deluge of material, for learning masses of numbers and formulae, for tackling problems, and for preparing written work. You will also find ways to read more efficiently and to make the most of your study time. There's even a section on what to do when things go wrong.

Update with Sam, Joel and Zoe

You've already met our three first year science students. Let's see how they are coping after the first week or two of their very first semester.

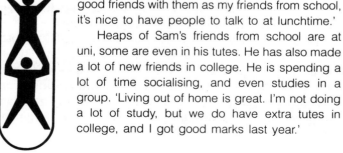

Joel is feeling a little lost. The only people he knows from school aren't really friends of his, and they're not doing his course, anyway. He joined some clubs in O-week, but he's a bit shy about going to their meetings. 'I'm a bit disappointed, I guess. I was really looking forward to coming to uni. I feel a bit left out, and I tend to go home straight after my classes.'

Because of the course she aims to do, Zoe has found herself in a group of students with the same timetable. She met some people on the first day, and she sees them a lot in her classes. 'Although I'm not as good friends with them as my friends from school, it's nice to have people to talk to at lunchtime.'

Heaps of Sam's friends from school are at uni, some are even in his tutes. He has also made a lot of new friends in college. He is spending a lot of time socialising, and even studies in a group. 'Living out of home is great. I'm not doing a lot of study, but we do have extra tutes in college, and I got good marks last year.'

LEARNING AS YOU GO

Where do I start?

Building on study success is an important part of adapting to a new learning environment. How does this work? Well, you have studied during earlier years and been successful; you succeeded in getting into university. This is both a bonus and a hurdle.

Success in previous study can help boost your confidence. However, because you have already had good study experiences, you may find it hard to adjust to the different needs of study at tertiary level: it can be hard to change a winning formula. Although you have developed a study style that answers the needs of secondary schooling, you will need to adapt it to fit the new demands at uni.

You're not a schoolkid any more—you're a professional student, an adult who is studying (if only you were making lots of money doing it!) as a full-time occupation. Some of you will study part time, but even so you need to approach it professionally.

PERSONAL LEARNING STYLES

At school, your learning was directed by others a lot more than it will be at uni. Your teachers made the decisions about how to break down the material to be learned. They also kept an eye on how much homework and study you were doing. At university, these responsibilities are now yours. So, how do you go about taking charge? First of all, it's probably useful to consider your own preferred learning style. One advantage of being responsible for your own learning is that you are free to consider your personal preferences.

Different people like to study in different ways

What are the characteristics of personal learning styles? Here are some examples:

- liking to try something 'hands on' before you fully understand it;
- being very good at visualising;
- preferring to talk something through with a friend to help you both understand it;
- preferring to study late at night, or early in the morning;
- using your computer for everything from notes to drafts to study timetables.

It's important to take these preferences into consideration, but you must also realise that it's a whole new world of study, and that you'll need to adapt.

Take some time to explore your study self

There are lots of ways you can find out more about your personal learning style. We've included a brief questionnaire at the end of this book (Appendix II). There are also lots of electronic resources that help you identify personal characteristics available via the internet: you can do online tests and get a brief evaluation. Two good places to start are the page of IQ and Personality tests on the web <http://www.2h.com/welcome.phtml> or you can try Yahoo! for some links <http://www.yahoo.com/Science/Psychology/>.

Once you have thought about your preferences, it's time to put them to work. Knowing a lot about your personal style is only helpful if you are also adapting and using good study techniques. Work from your strengths and be prepared to compensate for your weaknesses.

$$\frac{x + \frac{\pi}{4}}{\Omega - 2°C} \dashrightarrow$$

Joel says: 'I know I'm good at seeing the big picture, but sometimes I forget the detailed evidence needed to back up my generalisations. I guess I should spend more time studying examples.'

Zoe disagrees: 'I *like* to look at the fine detail, and I learn best when I can do lots of practice problems and see how the theory works for myself.'

Most of the assessment tasks you will face as a science student will require you to get involved with the material to be learned. It won't be enough to sit there like a sponge and hope to soak up ideas.

If you think about what we said in Chapter 1 about lecturers' expectations that students will be interested and willing to work on their own, you can understand why waiting for the information to come to you won't be enough. Engaging actively with the work you have to do involves questioning and evaluating your tasks. Sometimes, you'll have to make decisions about what's important, what you need to do more work on, and what you don't.

LEVELS OF UNDERSTANDING

Level 1: 'I've seen that before.'

You should think about how well you need to know the material that you are studying. There are different levels of 'knowing'. There's recognising something that you have experienced before: that's a very basic level of learning and not of special use at tertiary level. You may think that you can approach multiple choice exams with only this level of knowledge—'I'll know the right answer when I see it'—but it won't necessarily work. (See Chapter 10 on exams.)

Level 2: 'I can understand the beginning and the end, but not the middle.'

At the next level of knowing, you can remember bits of the whole idea, but you need prompting to complete it. This is a good stage to get to, because you can easily build on it. Doing some extra reading or a practice problem are a couple of ways to fill in those gaps.

> Zoe says: 'In my Zoology class, we were covering some of the same topics as I did in Year 12 Biology. The material was familiar, but the lecturer's approach was really different to my teacher's last year. I found it a bit confusing; the lecturer concentrated on giving us lots of information about experimental evidence, but I didn't feel like he was telling us any definite facts. We also moved through the subject really quickly. That was only two weeks ago, and now we're onto a totally new topic. I find I have to review my notes and read the textbook before I understand what he is saying.'

Level 3: 'I can tell you how this works.'

After getting to level 2, you can develop a knowledge of something that enables you to remember the whole of the idea. This means that you know how it works so well that you can explain it to someone else. You already have this level of knowledge for a great many things—the rules of your favourite sport, the plot of your favourite soapie, the legendary figures important in the history of your hobby. If you develop this level of knowledge in your science subjects, you'll do very well in assessments.

Level 4: 'We could use this idea over there, too.'

The highest level of knowing occurs when you have not only made the accepted ideas of the discipline part of your own knowledge base, but when you can adapt the ideas to new situations, or even develop them further through mentally manipulating them. This of course could lead you into new research areas, and is a great basis for honours or postgraduate study.

BECOMING AN ACTIVE LEARNER

In order to reach the higher levels of knowing, you need to become active with the material. Study techniques such as reading and re-reading the same information in the very same words, or writing out your notes over and over, are passive techniques. Sure, you will eventually learn the material, but at uni level, you won't have time to study this way. The same goes for underlining or highlighting parts of the texts or your notes—it implies that you're going to get time to go back over that passage before the exam. You'll discover that it's very hard to find any spare time at the end of the semester—swot vac just isn't long enough!

> Sam says: 'Some people in my science subjects spend all their time reading and memorising the textbook and their lecture notes. I want to get good marks, but I also

want to have a life. All that study sounds really boring to
me. Besides, won't I get stale on the material if I spend
all my time reading it over and over?'

Apart from being very time-consuming,
passive learning is boring. So dump it.

MORE GOOD THINGS ABOUT
ACTIVE LEARNING

First, it allows you to interact with the concepts you need
to learn, even if it's only mentally (yes, you can be mentally
active), and that means that study is much more interesting.
You must have experienced the stale feeling of having your
eyes read over the page from top left to bottom right, and
realising that nothing went further than your eyeballs, and
you need to read the whole page again. Active study will
prevent this because it makes your study more interesting.

Second, active learning is more time-efficient. Sure, some
of the things you do may take longer than just reading over
your notes. However, they are also more effective. You will
learn more in the same time, or the same amount in a
shorter time, which will be very handy for those of you
with very full timetables.

Third, active learning encourages you to think creatively
about the material. You will discover that at university level
there is not always one right answer that you need to know;
there will be multiple theories attempting to explain the
same phenomenon, different techniques to solve similar
problems, or a range of methods to tackle the same project.
Your task increasingly will be to analyse and evaluate
different applications to specific instances. Active learning
will help to stimulate your ability to do this because it
encourages analytical and creative thinking.

Of course, there will be basic facts that you need to

know before you can test various approaches against them. However, you need to remember that at university level, it is accepted that what we know now is not necessarily 'true'; it is a step on the journey of discovery.

For example, new 'facts' may be discovered tomorrow, maybe at the university where you are studying. Sure, there are the laws of gravity, but now there's also chaos theory. We learn all the time; knowledge is not static. Otherwise we'd still be studying how the other planets rotate around the Earth, or how dangerous it is for ships to sail over the horizon, where they could fall off the edge of the flat world!

Things that are good for your brain don't have to be boring. Be creative about your study—the more interesting you can make it, the more effectively you will learn. You can find some detailed practical suggestions for active study in Chapter 4.

IDEAS FOR COLLABORATIVE LEARNING

This leads us to collaborative learning. Many of your fellow students will be struggling under the same demanding workload as you are. It may be that, by pooling your resources, you can be of mutual benefit to each other. Even when attempting routine tasks such as tute sheets, you may find that working through the problems with a friend helps you both to solve them more quickly. Perhaps one of you is good at seeing how to approach the problem, and another is especially good at working through the formulae in detail, while someone else can show the rest of you useful short cuts for calculations.

It is often the case that you all know part of what to do, or how something works, but that not one of you knows everything at this stage. By combining forces, you can all learn how to attack the entire task, which will help all of you to succeed in your individual study sessions.

PUTTING ACTIVE LEARNING TO WORK

Keeping your learning active will also
help with managing your time. You
can get your work done efficiently if
you use active learning strategies
wisely. We'll talk more about time and
organisation in Chapter 3.

3 FINDING TIME TO STUDY

As we have said in previous chapters, success at university depends on more than just attending classes. For each hour of class time, you will need to put in at least an hour of study. (For some subjects, you may need more.) 'Study' in this case means preparing, reading, and reviewing your notes after class. If you have assignments or essays, you will need to budget extra time for them.

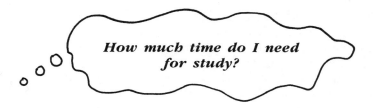

How much time do I need for study?

All of these study tasks will add up to quite a number of hours. As a rough guide, if you are studying full time, you should be putting in about 40 hours a week (including classes or *contact hours*). Towards the end of semester, and during swot vac, you may need to spend even more time studying.

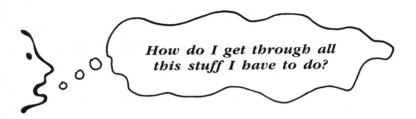

How do I get through all this stuff I have to do?

The best way to cope is to work steadily. It's important to keep abreast of what is happening in each of your courses; there is too much in each for you to leave studying until swot vac. Also, irregular bursts of frenzied study produce poor long-term learning gains. This means that you will do better if you organise your study time to occur often, in shorter rather than gigantic blocks of time, and don't forget those active learning strategies from Chapter 2.

Get into the DIN (do it now) habit. It's easier to remember something you encounter more than once within a short time-frame. So it's a good idea to look over new information as soon as you can. The same day is best; the same week is essential. Otherwise you'll be starting a new learning episode instead of building upon the one that began when you first heard the information. Attacking these study tasks immediately has lots of other advantages—it's a great procrastination breaker.

Keeping up every week is a golden rule of learning at tertiary level. Even if you don't cover all the week's work before you get something else new, do some work in each subject every week. It isn't necessary for you to know or even understand everything the first week that you encounter it.

On this point, it's important to realise that you're not stupid if you don't understand everything as soon as it is presented to you. The ideas and concepts presented at tertiary level are not simple: they're challenging and therefore interesting! And if you knew it all, you wouldn't be there to find out more. Be kind to yourself and allow yourself space to grow into the new ways of thinking.

IDEAS FOR TIME MANAGEMENT

You're probably asking yourself how you are going to fit in all this study, especially if you're like the majority of science students and have a full timetable of lectures, pracs and tutorials. And of course, like Sam, Joel and Zoe, you probably want to have a life that includes other things, and you probably have a part-time job, too. In fact, it is a good idea to do more than just go to lectures and the library. There is a wide range of other activities that should be incorporated into your weekly program.

> Zoe says: 'During the summer holidays I was working twenty hours a week as a shop assistant. I like having the money, but I can't cope with working that many hours and studying. I talked to my boss, and have cut down to only two shifts a week during semester. That's enough cash to get by.'

Organise, organise, organise

The first thing to do is to make a study timetable that will work for you. You probably have a lecture and tutorial timetable; this might have been given to you, or you may have filled it in yourself. Similarly, you might like to make a study timetable which indicates what sorts of things you will do in the spaces before and after classes.

Remember that you're approaching study as a full-time occupation. You are in fact much like a professional worker doing a 9–5 type of day. This also means that you should take a break for lunch, and for coffee (if you can) at some point. However, you don't have to do all your study between 9:00 a.m. and 5:00 p.m. You have some flexibility, and it's important to use your freedom wisely.

Organise your day to suit your habits

Think about the time of day when your regular study is taking place. Is there a time when you are better at focusing on tasks (morning, late at night?), and a time when you have trouble staying awake (after lunch)? Time your study to coincide with your more productive thinking hours.

Do this quick and easy exercise to evaluate your patterns of concentration. Draw a horizontal line which represents the hours of the day in which you are awake. Label each end with the appropriate time. Now, plot your energy level over the course of the day on the vertical axis.

Figure 3.1 My daily energy level

Are you studying at the time when your potential is highest?

You can maximise your study potential if you do difficult thinking tasks when you are freshest. For example, if your list of things to do includes writing an introduction for a prac report, photocopying some notes for a lecture you missed and doing a computer programming problem, then do the problem first. Save study 'housework' for times when you are too tired to do more complicated things. That way, even if you are not all that enthusiastic, you will still be doing something useful.

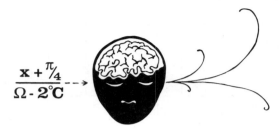

YOUR STUDY TIMETABLE

Figure 3.2 is an example of a blank timetable. You can photocopy this chart and fill it in, or make your own. Use lots of different coloured pens to indicate different activities, if you like. You can make a big chart, or use a smaller piece of paper that will fit in your diary. The important thing is to create a picture that makes sense to you. Be creative!

When you organise your timetable, keep these points in mind:

1. Start by filling in all your contact hours (tutes, lectures, pracs).
2. Put in all your other commitments (paid work, netball practice, household chores, favourite TV show). If your timetable looks full at this point, you may need to do a bit of thinking about the number of extra activities you are undertaking—there's lots more to go in yet.
3. Evaluate the 'spare' time remaining and think about your personal preferences. Be realistic. Don't block out 6:00–8:00 every morning for study if you don't get up till 9:00. Find a couple of hours in each day to use as study time.
4. Divide your study times into 30-minute blocks.
5. Don't just write 'study' in those blocks of time. Indicate for yourself exactly what you should be doing: 'read for Biology prac', 'do Physics problems', 'review Psych notes'.
6. Don't think of one- or two-hour gaps between classes as recess. Sure, you can have a coffee for half an hour,

	Monday	Tuesday	Wednesday	Thursday	Friday	Saturday	Sunday
8:00							
9:00							
10:00							
11:00							
12:00							
1:00							
2:00							
3:00							
4:00							
5:00							
6:00							
Evening							

Figure 3.2　A blank timetable

but use the rest of the time to do a little reading, review some notes or borrow library books.

7. Include some regular study times for revision and assignment work.

Figure 3.3 is an example of the classes that make up a first year science timetable. But this is not all you need to do in a week.

Figure 3.4 is a full timetable which includes activities, work and study times. This student does a number of extra activities, and lives at home with kind parents who don't require her to do a lot of chores.

Even if you aren't a timetable sort of person, it's a good idea to at least *try* using one, and to get into the habit of using your diary so you don't get ambushed by assignment due dates. At the very least, having a timetable makes you aware of what needs to be done. (You can also put a copy of your timetable on the fridge, so everyone knows about your study routines.)

If the timetable isn't working, then adapt it to your needs and preferences. Don't stick to it no matter what. A good timetable has room to accommodate disasters, and can be flexible.

MAKING BEST USE OF STUDY TIME

As we've suggested above, it is often better to think of your study in terms of tasks, not as slabs of time. It's more productive to say: 'At 11:00 a.m. I'll make my own flow chart of the ruminant digestive tract' than to say 'I'd better do some study for Biol'. In this way you can also increase you motivation; it feels good to finish a task, but it can be difficult to know when you've done enough 'study'.

It's also wise to keep in mind the old saying about 'all work and no play'. You really need—like a fully professional worker—to create a balanced lifestyle for yourself. If you've

	Monday	Tuesday	Wednesday	Thursday	Friday	Saturday	Sunday
8:00							
9:00		Biol 141 Lecture			Biol 141 Tute		
10:00	Chem 141 Prac	Biol 141 Prac	Chem 141 Tute	Physics 141 Prac			
11:00			Biol 141 Lecture		Biol 141 Lecture		
12:00					Physics 141 Tute		
1:00	LUNCH	LUNCH	LUNCH	LUNCH	LUNCH		
2:00	Psych 100 Lecture	Psych 100 Lecture		Psych 100 Lecture			
3:00	Chem 141 Lecture		Chem 141 Lecture	Chem 141 Lecture			
4:00							
5:00	Physics 141 Lecture		Physics 141 Lecture	Physics 141 Lecture			
6:00	Psych 100 Tutorial						
Evening							

Figure 3.3 Timetable of classes for a first year science course

	Monday	Tuesday	Wednesday	Thursday	Friday	Saturday	Sunday
8:00						**SOCCER**	
9:00	Prep for Chem prac	Biol 141 Lecture	(Finish prac work if needed)	(Finish prac work if needed)	Biol 141 Tute		
10:00	Chem 141 Prac (Lab 4)	Biol 141 Prac (1st year prac room)	Chem 141 Tute	Physics 141 Prac (Upper Lab)	Library photocopying **Coffee**		**WORK**
11:00			Biol 141 Lecture		Biol 141 Lecture	Review Biol	
12:00			Prep for Physics prac		Physics 141 Tute	Do Phych reading and assignments	
1:00	LUNCH	LUNCH	LUNCH (with movie club)	LUNCH	LUNCH (and library)		
2:00	Psych 100 Lecture	Psych 100 Lecture		Psych 100 Lecture	**WORK**		
3:00	Chem 141 Lecture	Do Chem tute work with Sam	Chem 141 Lecture	Chem 141 Lecture		Physics problems	
4:00	Do Psych tute work	Review lecture notes	Psych reading **Coffee**	Do Physics problems with Zoe			Prep for Biol prac
5:00	Physics 141 Lecture	Psych reading **Coffee**	Physics 141 Lecture	Physics 141 Lecture		Review Physics and Chem	
6:00	Psych 100 Tutorial	Work on Psych assignments		Review lecture notes and do		*Study and assignments if necessary or*	Biol review and assignments
Evening	Review lecture notes	**CHOIR**	Review lecture notes **X Files**	Biol tute work **Soccer Training**		**GO OUT**	TV and videos

Figure 3.4 A comprehensive weekly timetable

honestly done all the work you need to for the day, don't keep sitting at your desk. Have a break, and enjoy it.

You need regular exercise to keep healthy. This will help you to avoid the common colds and flu in winter—around exam time. It will also increase your metabolic rate—and if your body works more quickly, so will your brain. For the same reasons, you need a healthy diet and a sensible sleep pattern. If you're doing paid work as well, make sure you don't become too fatigued. The old 'healthy bodies make healthy minds'—it's true.

Giving yourself permission not to study (and not to feel guilty) is important, because a rest needs to be a real rest if it is going to refresh you. The key to a successful and fulfilling time at uni is a balanced, regular pattern of mixed activities and tasks that helps sustain your interest in life and enables you to continue developing your knowledge base.

A WORD ABOUT PROCRASTINATION

All students are procrastinators, some are just a lot better at managing their problem than others. Because most of your deadlines seem a long way off, it's easy to put off study in order to play tennis or go to the pub for the afternoon. However, if procrastination about study gets to be a habit, you can find yourself in deep trouble at the end of semester.

The time management ideas we have suggested in this chapter will help you to develop good study habits. The best way to beat procrastination is to do a little bit every day; because the longer you put things off, the harder it is to get going. Remember, motivation is a key to successful study, and you can only stay motivated and interested if you are involved in doing your work. Inertia can be a big trap.

If you are finding it hard to settle down to study, you might need to adjust your study environment. Some people find it easier to work where other people are also studying.

Are there fewer distractions if you study in the library rather than at home? If you find the atmosphere of hard work is a good influence on you, then organise to stay at uni a bit later (or get in early) and do your work in the library.

Procrastination sometimes involves your physical environment (you know—wandering around, cleaning the house, arranging your study space); likewise, there are things you can do to attune your senses to study. A well-organised study space, one that is organised to suit you, can help to settle you into study mode. Get in the habit of dumping everything you need on the desk before you sit down—this will discourage aimless wandering. Some people like to play specific study music to help focus their thoughts; they play these pieces each time they work. There are theories about Baroque music encouraging a studious mindset . . . you might prefer something else. You can try aromatherapy, too—some essential oils like clary sage, citrus and basil are said to enhance concentration.

Get help from other people. Explain to the people you live with the level of nagging you need; sometimes reminders from other people will just make you more stressed. Collaborative learning can help you get your study habits on track—organise to meet a friend, and make a pact not to tempt one another to procrastinate. Tutors, lecturers and learning skills advisers can also help you by giving you deadlines to hand in drafts of your work. This strategy not only gets the work done before time, it helps you to improve the final product.

Do I need a study buddy?

This may sound like an odd one, but . . . if you are going to stop studying for the day, don't finish what you are doing. It is often a lot easier to get going on something you have to finish than something you have to start. If you leave your reading with one or two pages to go, then you have something to start with the next day. You will probably find that once you have sat down to do this little bit, you feel ready to start on the next task.

At the end of every study session, make a note of what you were thinking or doing, and leave your books open on your desk (if possible). Lots of procrastination occurs as stalling before you sit down and fidgeting once you have sat down. If you leave yourself something definite to get back to, and a pointer to the important concepts you were thinking about, you will make it a lot easier to take up where you left off. Of course, the more quickly you return to study, the more effective this strategy will be.

Active learning is a big help with time management. Try to have specific goals and interesting ways to accomplish them when you sit down at your desk. Study time will breeze by, and you'll get lots of work done.

Still looking for more ideas? Check out some online study skills advice. The Learning Skills Unit at the University of Melbourne <http://www.services.unimelb.edu.au/lsu> and The Learning Development Centre at the University of Western Sydney (Macarthur) <http://www.macathur.uws.edu.au/ssd/ldc/Resources.html> are good places to start.

HOW TO REMEMBER WHAT YOU'VE LEARNED

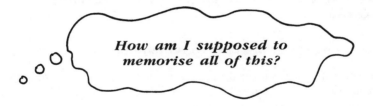

How am I supposed to memorise all of this?

The most common study problem science students face is dealing with an enormous amount of material. You will probably find yourself with what seems like a mountain of things to remember. You have so many formulae, lists and tables to learn, but you can't begin to study because you're working through so many examples and tutorial sheets. Don't despair, there are things that can help. We know how important active learning is. In this chapter, we'll look at how to apply those active learning ideas to specific types of material that you need to remember.

You might be wondering why we have decided to discuss study and memory at this early stage—don't exams happen at the end of semester? The answer is that consolidating knowledge into memory takes time. The sooner you start, the better.

Feeling overburdened with work and a little confused is a common problem for first year students. Partly that's because of issues such as those we discussed in Chapter 1: the amount of material, the quick pace of delivery, the large class sizes and the lack of individual supervision. But you can learn to adapt to all of these as long as you are prepared to be flexible about the way you tackle the study tasks. For example, you may have done extremely well in your last years at high school by putting in long hours going over and over your textbooks and exercises. Now you find that at university level there just isn't enough time to use that study technique effectively. So what can you do?

TAKING ADVANTAGE OF THE WAY MEMORY WORKS

Interesting things are easy to remember

We know that repeating things over and over (rote learning) is one way to remember them, but there are other factors that help us to make and retain permanent data stores. For example, if you are really interested in something, you have no trouble remembering all the details about it. Most people have no difficulty remembering the plot intricacies of a favourite book, film, or TV show. You can probably remember the detailed and complex rules of your favourite hobby, sport or computer game. Because you are *motivated* to know these things, they are easy to recall.

If it makes sense, you will remember it better

Another element of memory is *understanding*. If you know how something works, you can easily recall the details without learning them off by heart, because you can relate the different sections to one another. So understanding a concept will help you to remember it. When you first learned the 12 times table it was a collection of numbers. When you began to understand the concept, the numbers made sense because you understood how they relate to each other.

Patterning and linking aid memory

Along the same line, if you can appreciate how a certain system is organised, then you can more easily recall the separate parts that contribute to that system. We find it easier to remember items that we can fit neatly into categories, because we like to see (or imagine) *patterns* in the data. Therefore being able to organise the information coherently will aid memory. When you made connections and saw the patterns in the times tables (for example, 12 x 5 is the same as 5 x 12), they were much easier to remember.

Similarly, *linking* items together will help you to remember them. If you can't see an overall pattern, perhaps you can see a similarity to something you already know. Associating one idea with another known idea will aid recall. Associations can be simple (like remembering that Italy is shaped like a boot) or more complex (such as associating the notion of bacterial resistance to antibiotics with Darwinian survival theory).

Visualisation is another key to memory

Finally, if we consider the sensory material that we are receiving, we realise that most of what we learn reaches us through sight. Having the ability to *visualise* something enhances memory, and being able to visualise something in a three-dimensional image is an even stronger enhancement.

These principles are summarised in Table 4.1.

How can I apply these ideas?

Table 4.1 Elements of remembering

Element of memory	How it works
Motivation	You remember items that you are really interested in remembering
Understanding	You remember items that you comprehend
Patterning	You remember items that you can arrange coherently
Linking	You remember items that you can associate with other, known ideas
Visualising	You remember items of which you have a clear visual image

The rest of this chapter will show you how to apply what we know about memory to the specific memory tasks that science students are faced with. These learning tasks can be broken into three main types: 'list' information that you feel you need to learn by rote; practical skills for performing procedures; and theoretical concepts that you need to understand.

Unfortunately, they all require mental effort. The easier a memory technique sounds, the less likely it is to be really effective, particularly for learning at tertiary level. In this section, we'll describe some techniques for improving memorisation. None of them is magical. However, used sensibly, and with thought, they will help you to improve your ability to recall information in exams.

MEMORISATION OF LISTS

There are quite a few ways to tackle information that you need to know 'by heart'. The first of these is to treat the material as something you need to understand; in this case, you can become active with the material so that you can appreciate how it works. Make sense of information and learn actively.

For example, if you need to learn the names of the twelve cranial nerves, you could rework the list as it is presented in your textbook so that the nerves are grouped according to function, or nerve type. You could make yourself familiar with the Latin or Greek origins of the names and use this to help you understand why each nerve is named as it is and what function it performs. You can visit the anatomy museum and see the specimens presented there so that you have a clear idea of where the nerves exit and where they are headed (this could help you form a 3-D image as well). You could practise drawing the nerves freehand and writing the names and actions on each image. Understanding the functions of the nerves will aid memory.

Another way to tackle lists is to use some type of mnemonic. Some 'memory experts' use devices such as the method of loci or peg words to help them remember meaningless lists of numbers or words. The method of loci involves visualising a series of places, always in the same order, and mentally placing the items to be learned one by one at each of those locations. Peg words also must be used in order (you 'peg' a visual image to a number—one, bun; two, shoe; etc—and then attach the listed items to each visual image).

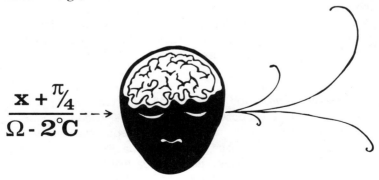

Another type of mnemonic is to make 'pretend sense' out of the otherwise seemingly meaningless data. You can make a word, a sentence or a poem that helps you remember the information. Examples of this are Roy G Biv for the colours of the rainbow (red, orange . . .), or Every Good Boy Deserves Fruit for the lines of the treble clef in music. Using the twelve cranial nerves example, you may already know the sentence 'On Old Olympus' Towering Top . . . etc' and that may help you remember the sequence of names (though you have to be careful you don't get the 'o' words out of order, as Clare did for one exam!).

Most of the popular 'memory enhancement' books you see on the paperback shelves go into quite a bit of detail about using such devices to remember information. Use your commonsense and don't believe everything the ads say without question. While these schemes have their place at university level, sometimes the techniques take so long to master that you could have spent the time more profitably learning the data itself. Another point to keep in mind is that using mnemonics such as peg words requires regular revision or repetition of the same items, so that it can be quite a time-consuming exercise altogether.

Some students like to flood their environments with reminders of the items to be learned. You can write the list out and put copies of it in a multitude of places such as the back of the bathroom door, on the fridge, above your desk . . . You can make a tape of the list and play it in your car or walkman . . . You can draw diagrams and tables and hide them in your lunch . . .

Sam asks about 'sleep learning': 'I've heard that if you play tapes while you sleep, you can memorise what you hear. You are supposed to learn really well even though you don't realise it's happening. Think about it—all that wasted sleep time used for study instead!'

Unfortunately, there's no evidence that this is going to help. Do you really want to take the chance? However,

it is important to get plenty of rest when you are studying—memory is impaired by fatigue.

One way to learn lists that students have found useful is to
put the words into a (mostly) coherent form that can be
sung to a tune they already know. You could try the twelve
cranial nerves sung to the tune of 'The Twelve Days of
Christmas'! This association of new material with a well-es-
tablished framework helps organise the material, and that
helps you to remember it. Table 4.2 summarises the techniques you can use to learn lists of items.

REMEMBERING PROCEDURES

Learning lists of items is only one of the many remembering
tasks that face science students. Another is the need to
remember how to perform certain practical procedures, such
as laboratory tests or clinical examinations. You will find
that an examination of your skills in these areas will form
a part of your assessment in many science subjects. For
many students, the prospect of being tested in practical skills
can be terrifying.

Students may try to use some of the techniques listed
above to help them remember how to perform their practical
tasks. That is, they may make a list of the steps that need
to be performed in order to carry out, for example, an
examination of lower limb muscle function. Or they may
say over and over the sequence of steps needed for a
laboratory assay. The main problem with these approaches
to learning practical tasks is that, essentially, you won't be
practising the competency you'll be tested in. The examiner
probably won't ask you to *say* what should happen next:
you'll be expected to *do* it. Think about what will be tested.

The key to doing well in practical examinations is to
make yourself as familiar as possible with the technique/s
that you will need. Practise actually doing your tasks. If

Table 4.2 Techniques for learning lists of items

Technique	How to use it	Example	Use it for	Disadvantages
Understanding	Become active with the material	Group listed items by a different principle	Parts of a system or theory	You need to be inventive
Visual mnemonics	Learn a sequence of visual images and mentally attach the list items to the images	Picture each member of your family holding one element of a formula	Lists of items with weak connections to each other	1. You need to learn the pegs 2. You have to revise the visual images often
Word game mnemonics	Make a word or sentence from the first letters of list items	Roy G Biv knows all the colours of the rainbow	Lists of items that need to be remembered in order	1. You have to be inventive 2. You have to revise the mnemonic often
Environmental cues	Put reminders or copies of the data that you need to know in a place where you will see/hear them often	Photocopy the table of elements and cover your folder with it	Especially for diagrams or pictorial representations	You need to change the items often or you stop noticing them; you still need to treat information actively
Melody association	Make the words of the items that you need to know fit into the lyrics of a song	Learn the bones of the upper limb by singing them to 'Dem Bones'	Lengthy lists where connections or functions of the items are important	1. You may run out of suitable melodies 2. You may confuse the lists with the real lyrics of the song

there are certain clinical or laboratory procedures that you need to know, your best way of tackling them is to practise doing them. It's a little like learning to drive: it's fine to rehearse to yourself 'ease off the clutch, ease down on the accelerator, release the handbrake', but as long as you need to say these words over to yourself as you perform a hill start, you'll be less than a completely competent driver. When you can perform the task without consciously thinking about it, you will appear much more confident and impressive to the examiner.

Achieving the necessary amount of practice can be problematic. Often labs and prac rooms are either fully booked with classes or closed and locked at other times. In some places, there will be an overload of students and you will find that you need to share the facilities even during your scheduled practical times. This can make it very difficult for you to become really familiar with the equipment so that the procedures become second nature.

However, if you are enthusiastic and inventive, you can create practice sessions for yourself. Some of the latest brain activity studies show that when you mentally imagine yourself performing an activity, you in fact stimulate most of the areas of brain tissue that would be involved in the activity itself. So instead of (or as well as) saying the steps over to yourself, you should strive for a mental image of yourself actually performing each of the steps in sequence.

Another way of achieving the desired competence with a procedure is to practise it in the absence of the equipment while still performing the necessary movements. This is a bit like reading a dance score—but instead of just saying 'first I have to step to the right, then there's a twist, and then there's a half-slide backwards', you read or say the step and then act it out. This can be useful, too, for practising clinical examination techniques. In this case, you can enlist a fellow student as a 'patient' and you can practise the exam on each other even if you don't have the necessary equipment at your fingertips.

The point to remember is that for a practical task, you must enlist your 'physical' or kinaesthetic memory, as well as verbal and auditory, to get the best results. Going through the movements may not sound useful, but it will bring very good results. Table 4.3 gives a summary of ways to study practical tasks.

LEARNING AND UNDERSTANDING THEORY

The third type of material you need to learn is the theory. Learning theoretical concepts can be very challenging, particularly when you have a great many of them thrust at you all at once, or when learning a new concept depends upon your understanding of a previous one about which you don't feel very sure.

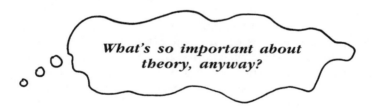

What's so important about theory, anyway?

It's important to come to grips with theory, though, because theories help scientists to organise ideas. Once you understand the principles, other things may fall into place. Why is this? Well, as we said before, understanding concepts and organisation of ideas are keys to memory. For example, the organisaton of the elements in the original periodic table was done on the basis of practical experience of their properties. Students had to learn the table off by heart. Now knowledge of atomic structure provides the theoretical underpinning for the organisation of the periodic table. If you learn these principles, you can figure out which element goes where without memorising every one.

Table 4.3 Techniques for studying prac tasks

Technique	How to use it	Example	Use it for	Disadvantages
Listing the steps	Write the steps of a procedure in sequence and memorise it	Isolate the steps of preparing a microscopic slide and say them over to yourself	Getting the steps into the right order	1. You need to do a lot of repetition 2. You're not practising the actual procedure
Mentally performing the activity	As you say the steps, visualise yourself doing each one	Create a mental image of your hands preparing the slide	Times when you can't physically practise the task	You need a bit of imagination to do it
Rehearsing the routine	As you read the steps of the procedure, mime doing them	Make the movements you would make if you really had the slide in your hands	Getting a feel for the physical activity	You mightn't feel comfortable doing this in the library!
Acting out the task	Work with a partner and act out the examination on each other	Examine the reflexes of the foot or lower limb on each other	Good for physical examinations or learning anatomy	1. It might be difficult to find a partner 2. You may get embarrassed

Table 4.4 Techniques for learning theory

Technique	How to use it	Example	Use it for	Disadvantages
Mind maps	Start with writing the central theme in the middle of the page, and develop sub-ideas around it	Write 'cell division' and draw lines from it to related words	Helping to visualise the components of a complex theory	1. You need to be creative 2. The ideas may look disorganised and therefore hard to remember
Summaries	Read a section or chapter and then write a summary of the main ideas	Write point form lists of the elements of the 'Big Bang' theory	Helps to organise parts of a theory into a shorter form	1. You may find it hard to use your own words 2. You may end up copying and not being active
Changed format	Make the theory look different by working it into another format	Use a flow chart to describe the elements involved in the process of glycolysis	Sequencing elements in a described or proposed theoretical explanation	1. You have to be inventive to change the look 2. You have to be careful to include all elements
Populist-speak	Practise explaining the theory in different words	Imagine that your little sister asked what quarks are—see if you can write it simply	Making sure that you've understood how the theory works as an explanation	1. It's hard to use your own words 2. You may need help to understand it first

Collaboration	Ask fellow students to form a study group—run it with definite aims	Work on old tute sheets and take turns starting and finishing problems	Tasks that you often 'get stuck' on	1. Others may not be ready to work 2. Some people may take advantage of your work
Disappearing data	Make copies of the material to be learned, white-out different elements on each copy, and then complete them from memory	Write out the formula for calculating the heat produced by dielectric heating, copy it, white-out symbols and try to re-create it	Theoretical explanations where each element contributes essential processes	1. It might be costly 2. You need to leave some time between preparing the sheets and finishing them
Examiner hat	Pretend you are the examiner and create questions from the theoretical material	Read over the section on the action of the superior and inferior rectus muscles and create a short-answer question	Useful towards the end of the semester when you should be trying to see the material from various perspectives	Perhaps you find it hard to act like an examiner!
Dress rehearsal	Get hold of old exam papers and sit parts of them under exam conditions	'Sit' the first 40 minutes of the biology exam with no coffee or music	Preparing your mind and body for the exam 'marathon'	You may find it difficult to get old papers

For theoretical concepts, all of the active study principles we discussed in Chapter 2 will be useful. Remember that the emphasis is on mental work with the ideas, not merely cramming as many words as possible into your head. As a reminder (which is a good thing to have in a chapter on remembering!), Table 4.4 provides a summary of some of the active study principles that would be suitable for learning theories.

> Joel says: 'I made some friends in my Psychology lab class because we had to do a group presentation. We have a test next week, and we have decided to do some study in a group, because we work well together. I find that talking about ideas with other people helps me to understand and remember. We studied method of loci in one of our Psych labs, and our experiment results showed that it does help, at least for remembering lists of words. Now my study group is trying to think of ways to use this memory trick in our study for the test.'

So you see there are many ways to learn material, and memorising items 'off by heart' may not be the most appropriate way to go. Use a variety of techniques tailored to the type of material to be learned, so that you stay mentally fresh. Studying can be hard work (so can playing sport) but it is possible to employ a range of learning (training) activities that enable you to enjoy that work.

You can find more hints about memory techniques on the World Wide Web. Check out 'Mind Tools— Memory Techniques and Mnemonics' at <http://www.bazis.nl/personal/vermey/memory.html>.

5 NEW SKILLS

NOTE TAKING IN LECTURES AND LABS

THE PURPOSE OF NOTES

In your classes, you will be expected to take notes of the information that is given and what occurs during the class. The main reason for taking notes is to help you concentrate, and later to remember the important ideas and procedures that were used. Notes are useful study tools and can help you organise your understanding of the concepts. Also, you will find that most other people in the class are taking notes and you won't want to be left out.

Sometimes you won't *need* to take notes. For example, in lectures, a great deal of theory will be displayed and discussed. Perhaps you were given a course outline at the start of the year which contains a complete set of notes for the course. Sometimes lecturers hand out copies of their overhead slides at the lecture. When this happens, you may feel that there is no need for you to take your own notes. Sometimes you may feel it's better to listen carefully, rather than writing just for the sake of it.

In tutorials, laboratory or practical classes, you will have your prac book or weekly tute sheet to refer to, and you may feel that this is sufficient information to keep as a study aid. A few jottings of changes to the day's program may be all that you want to write.

So, should I take notes?

These are quite good reasons not to take notes, and there's no law that says you must take notes. However, taking notes does have a few advantages that you might like to consider:

- it keeps you awake;
- it forms a permanent record;
- it helps with later study;
- you can put the ideas into your own words;
- you can use them for discussion with other students;
- you can use them as a basis for writing reports, essays and assignments.

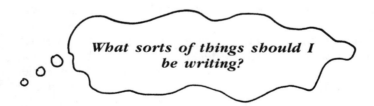

What sorts of things should I be writing?

Good notes are brief, and designed to jog your memory. When you take notes, you shouldn't be trying to get down every word that is said. It's not an exercise in dictation. Notes are to help clarify the major points and to help you remember them later.

Focus your ideas when you are taking notes. Write the topic and date of the lecture at the top of the page, and pay attention to what the lecturer tells you are the main points. Listen for 'signposts' and use headings, subheadings and numbering—this will help keep your notes on track and organised.

Sometimes notes can be questions or instructions for yourself. Believe it or not, writing comments like 'This is confusing', or 'This comes from Chapter 3', are often useful later. If you are reviewing your notes as part of your study, these sorts of notes can remind you of connections you need to make, or information you need to look up.

NOTE TAKING IN LECTURES

For lectures, you can write outlines for yourself or you can add comments to the printed notes that are provided. In labs and tutes, you can jot down the good (memorable) examples and any short cuts to procedures or calculations that your tutor/demonstrator tells you about.

SOME DIFFERENT STRATEGIES FOR NOTE TAKING

Different people take notes in a great variety of ways. Some use a rather complex 'mind map' strategy, where the main idea is written in the centre of the page and the related points branch away from it. Others are perfectly organised with ruled margins, colour-coded headings and neat dot points. Some notes are scrawls that even the author can't decipher a week later. The main point to remember about note taking is that it matters very little what shape your notes take: the important issue is what you do with the notes afterwards. You can take the most classy-looking notes, but if they moulder at the bottom of your aerobics bag for six months, they are of very little value to you.

Figures 5.1, 5.2 and 5.3 are examples of different note taking styles for different people and different circumstances.

Therefore

$$\oint \vec{B}.\vec{ds} = 0$$

is Gauss' Law in magnetism

Gauss = 10^{-4} Tesla

Motion of charged particle in B field.

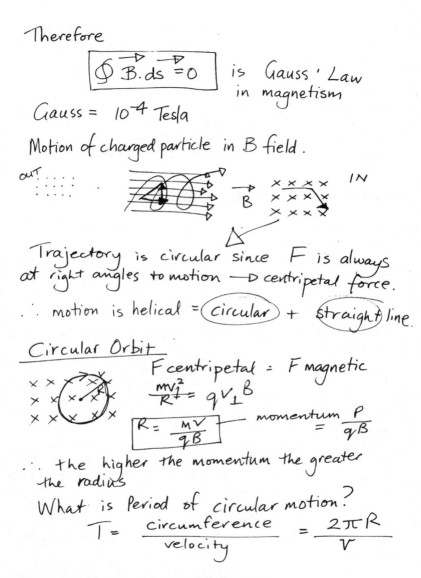

Trajectory is circular since F is always at right angles to motion $\rightarrow$ centripetal force.

∴ motion is helical = (circular) + (straight) line.

Circular Orbit

F centripetal = F magnetic

$$\frac{mv_\perp^2}{R} = qv_\perp B$$

$$R = \frac{mv}{qB}$$

momentum $\frac{P}{qB}$

∴ the higher the momentum the greater the radius

What is Period of circular motion?

$$T = \frac{\text{circumference}}{\text{velocity}} = \frac{2\pi R}{V}$$

Figure 5.1   Notes on theory, with diagrams

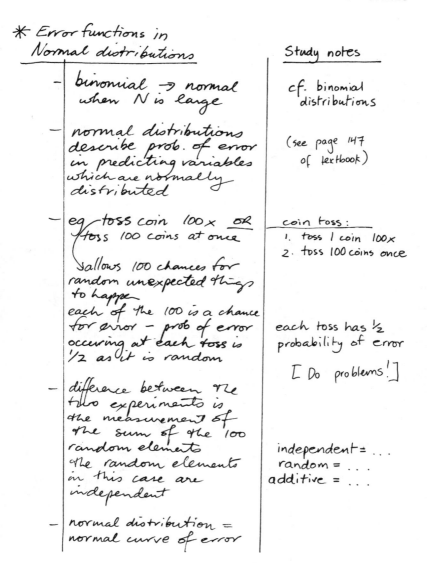

* Error functions in Normal distributions

Study notes

- binomial → normal when N is large

  cf. binomial distributions

- normal distributions describe prob. of error in predicting variables which are normally distributed

  (see page 147 of textbook)

- eg toss coin 100x <u>OR</u> toss 100 coins at once

  <u>coin toss:</u>
  1. toss 1 coin 100x
  2. toss 100 coins once

  allows 100 chances for random unexpected things to happen
  each of the 100 is a chance for error - prob of error occuring at each toss is ½ as it is random

  each toss has ½ probability of error

  [Do problems!]

- difference between the two experiments is the measurement of the sum of the 100 random elements
  the random elements in this case are independent

  independent = . . .
  random = . . .
  additive = . . .

- normal distribution = normal curve of error

Figure 5.2 Notes with a column of comments made during revision

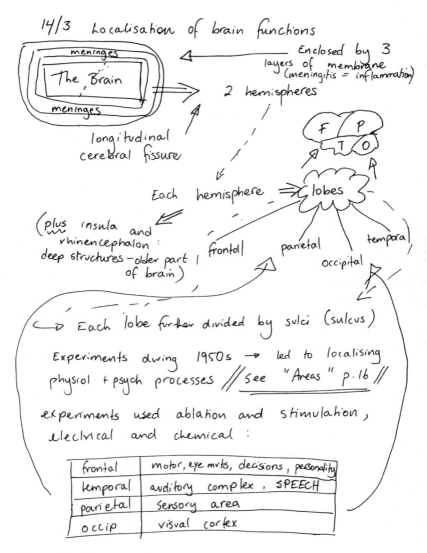

Figure 5.3: Notes made in a 'mindmap' style with connecting arrows for links

And don't fall into the trap of developing the world's best-ever note taking system, with add-on extras in the form of colour-codes, bullet points, boxes, fancy margins and so on: you could get so carried away with your beautiful creation that you neglect to listen to the ideas that are being discussed. Notes are only 'beautiful' if they are useful.

Who writes the "best" notes?

In Chapters 1 and 2, we talked about using study techniques that suit *you*, rather than trying to do what someone else does. Lots of students get trapped into thinking that someone else's notes are 'perfect'—neater, more accurate, written in better handwriting, clearer . . . You may have also heard that the grass is always greener on the other side of the fence. Keep in mind your own preferences. There's nothing wrong with experimenting with different note taking techniques, but you should settle fairly quickly on a style that suits you, and stick to it.

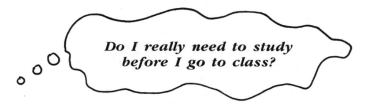

Do I really need to study before I go to class?

PREPARATION

Here are some ideas about how to get the most out of note taking. In Chapters 2 and 4 we talked about the ways we like to remember new ideas (being attentive, reviewing early etc). Because of the ways we remember, it's a good idea to do some preparation before the class. Ideally, you should do this immediately before each lecture, but often that's just not possible. If you have a very full day of classes, you might need to do your preparation the night before.

For a lecture, preparation may mean reading some of the source material that was suggested the previous week. It may be reading a chapter (or part of a chapter) of the main text. (We'll discuss approaches to reading in more detail in the next chapter.) It should at least consist of reading the title of the day's lecture before you arrive! Having even this small amount of work done will help you feel more comfortable with the topic of the lecture. That way, you'll understand the material more easily, and take better notes.

KEEPING ON TRACK

During the class, it can be difficult to concentrate unless you give yourself a definite task. Taking notes, or writing comments on your set of printed notes as you follow the lecture, will help your mind to stay actively involved with the concepts. You may find that what the lecturer talks about in the lecture is slightly different from what is in the printed notes, so you need to add points or draw connecting lines. In fact, you can take notes on your notes.

You may find, for example, that you can come up with a neat diagram that connects the ideas, and you can sketch it in the margin. It is essential to follow attentively any example that is worked through during the lecture, and recording it in written form will help you to focus on it. Again, don't be shy about recording your own comments and reactions in your notes.

Not all, or even many, of your notes from lectures will be in perfect sentence form—you're much more likely to be jotting diagrams, formulae, graphs or calculations than writing well-formed paragraphs. So your page might look a bit messy; that's fine, because as long as you review the ideas quickly, it doesn't matter how inconsistent your colour-coding is!

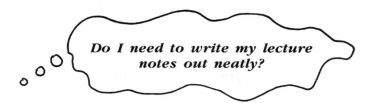

Do I need to write my lecture notes out neatly?

When you review, you should clarify any bits of writing that are *truly* illegible. An advantage of reviewing early (you should be reviewing your notes within 24 hours) is that you have some chance of remembering what it was you wrote. But don't waste time writing out everything again. If your handwriting is so bad you really need to retype your notes, then make the retyping an active learning experience. Summarise, describe, write things in your own words and make cross-references to other materials (readings, previous lectures, labs).

NOTE TAKING AND PREPARATION FOR OTHER CLASSES

To prepare for a tutorial or a lab, it's essential to read ahead so that you know what the class is about. Often there will be practical activities to be performed in the class, so you can save yourself a lot of time in the lab or prac room by being ready with what you have to do. Your time in labs is usually limited (there are never quite enough hours to complete the exercise) and you should make the most of this limited resource—use it for the practical exercise (that's a chance for some active learning, after all), not for reading.

You can save time by making sure you can identify each piece of apparatus. Do you need to know how to use the equipment beforehand, or will the demonstrator show you? If you familiarise yourself with the method for the lab, you will be aware of any confusing points in the description of the procedure and can be one of the first to claim the demonstrator's attention.

NOTE TAKING IN THE LABORATORY

During practical classes or tutorials, it's useful to jot down the little tips about procedures that the tutor or demonstrator will give you. If you've prepared yourself for the prac by reading through the appropriate part of the manual beforehand, you will be able to get straight down to the exercise for that day.

Get used to taking notes as you work. There will be pro forma reports or question sheets to complete as you go through the prac, so you should become accustomed to working with a pen handy. Most scientists do!

You will probably work in a small group of 4–6 students during your prac classes. It's important for everyone in the group to get as much experience with the equipment and procedures as is possible in the time allowed. Don't volunteer to take all the notes all the time: make sure the duties within the group are shared fairly. There are often one or two people in the group who want to hog all the equipment—insist as a group that everyone has fair turns. You can learn a lot more by doing rather than just watching, so make sure you have a go at everything you can. If your group is uncooperative about sharing responsibilities and experience, speak to your demonstrator.

MORE ABOUT NOTE TAKING AND ACTIVE LEARNING

Remember that all your classes—lectures, labs, tutes, pracs, seminars—are opportunities for learning. They are not arranged just to keep you off the streets and out of the cafe. They are not there to fill in time. If you do a little preparation, stay focused during the class, and manage to complete a related active learning task after each class, you'll be well on the way to good grades. Once again, a little work often is the key to performing well.

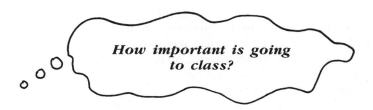

How important is going to class?

It's important to be on time—most lecturers set out their themes and begin the lecture with an overview. Then they present details and examples; the lecture will finish with a summary. If you miss the overview, the rest of the lecture may be confusing. In addition, some lectures are continuations of the previous day's (or week's). You won't figure this out if you always come in five minutes late.

A small point that may be worth mentioning here is that it is not essential to attend every class on your timetable, every week. Of course it's great if you do, but remember that these classes are not your only source of information. You have texts and course notes and staff, friends and journals and past papers to refer to. There's no need to panic if you miss something; do something active to make up for it.

However, you should not get haphazard about class attendance. Assessment in science subjects will test your knowledge of the whole semester's work. A lot of what you learn is building on previous classes. If you miss something, you will have to catch up—the sooner the better.

CARE AND FEEDING OF NOTES

Even the best notes need care and attention if they are going to work for you. The first step is early review to consolidate material into your long-term memory. It's also a good idea to review your notes when you finish a particular topic within your subjects—this gives you a good chance to fill in any gaps.

Later on, notes can be turned into useful study tools, though by themselves they may have limited value. You can use them to revise concepts and to form the basis for some of that 'changed format' activity that we spoke of in the previous chapter, but they can't leap into your head in perfect form all on their own. You need to do something with them. Make every note you take worthwhile.

6

NEW
SKILLS

READING

We've been talking a lot about the need for you to work outside class time in order to gain good marks. Reading will form the basis of the study you do on your own. Although you may not be marked on it, good reading will help you to do well in all of your assessment tasks.

Do I have to read all these articles?

You should be aware that not all of the material you ought to know is in your course notes; you will be expected to read from a wide range of sources. Not all of your reading needs to be approached as a lengthy chore; some of it can be done quite quickly. Also, not all of it is important or even essential: you need to prioritise and to use the time available for reading to the best advantage. Table 6.1 shows some of the sources of written information.

University students consult many sources because, at this level, we recognise that there may not be one right and true answer to every scientific question. In fact, you should

Table 6.1 Some of the sources of written information

Type of source	Who writes it?	What does it contain?	Where can I get it?
Textbook	One or more authors, usually academics	Multiple chapters organised by topics, as well as tables and diagrams	Departmental or faculty library, or buy one (they tend to be expensive)
Academic journal (a magazine published regularly)	Researchers and academics	A collection of research articles (reports on experiments) by various authors	Departmental or faculty library, or subscribe to it, some are available online, e.g. *Nature* <http://www.nature.com/>
Specialist book or monograph	An academic or group of academics	Detailed information on one topic	Library
Course outline and course notes	The course coordinator	Titles of lectures, information on assessments, study notes	Department or faculty office, university bookstore
Prac manual	Course coordinator or department	Details of weekly experiments, background material	Department or faculty office, university bookstore
Newspaper	Various journalists	Information about new projects or explanations of scientific processes	Widely available; your newsagent may get specialist papers for you
Internet	Wide range of writers	Information on recent developments	You may have access at home or through the computer lab

be aware that different circumstances affect different cases—there are exceptions, there are sets of data that are incomplete, there are theories that are nearly impossible to test. In addition to all that, nothing stays the same for long. There are astonishing new discoveries that happen regularly. Of course, along with all this, we know that there are 'facts' which are accepted by the broadest range of the scientific community, and which we need to learn.

READING FOR DIFFERENT PURPOSES

Reading at university level is not a single task: it has multiple faces and is useful for different purposes. Your curriculum at university level is much wider than at school level, and the reading you are required to do reflects this. It is unreasonable to expect that all the answers to all the questions, and all the explanations of all the concepts can be contained within the covers of a single textbook. Therefore you'll need to do reading from a range of sources and for completing different tasks.

The more reading you do, the more understanding you will have of a subject. However, a deeper understanding often means you have more questions than you have answers. Sometimes it's important to explore the details, at other times an overview is all you need.

There are four main reasons for reading academic texts:

- to preview a class,
- to prepare for a laboratory or practical session,
- to find information on topics that you are researching for a report or essay, and
- to 'study' or learn material before exams.

You will probably come to the conclusion that any reading list you are given is too long! Reading lists are often quite extensive and give more than one source for the same information. It's not the end of the world if you don't get to read all the recommended readings every week—in fact it would take a very long time to do so, longer than you probably have. So you need to make some choices about priorities. Obviously, you will be more prepared and do better if you manage to read some or even one of the recommended readings. You can use the following skimming (previewing) techniques to help save time.

PREVIEWING

Basically, *previewing* means finding out what's in the reading material before you read it. This is a good way to prepare for a lecture and the reading doesn't need to be ponderous and deep: you can do quite effective previews by skimming the material.

Previewing saves time and money

The purpose of previewing is to familiarise you with the reading matter—to help you decide if you need to read in more detail. As we know from Chapter 4, being familiar with the material can help with understanding it. Previewing can also help you to decide whether to photocopy—so it's a good idea to preview before you hit the 'print' button.

When you're skimming, you will read some of the material but not every word. It's handy, then, to know that most scientific writing follows certain conventional rules, such as having the main topic sentence of each paragraph as the first sentence of that paragraph. Reading just these 'topic' sentences will give you a good idea of what the whole piece is about, and save you lots of time.

Another convention of scientific writing is a liking for headings, subheadings, tables, and point-form lists. It's a good idea, before any reading task, to first read these through to the end of the section so that you know what to expect. Headings can give you clues about what you need to read, and what you don't. For example, if you see the headings 'Results' and 'Method' you can guess you are looking at a report on an experiment.

> Sam says: 'I had to read an article about the way fish hear. The first two pages described a theory of fish hearing in great detail, so I took heaps of notes. But then I got to page 3, and there was this heading which said something about *current* theories of fish hearing. So all the stuff I had notes on was a discussion of an old theory—and I was supposed to be answering a lab question about recent developments. What a waste of time!'

By first reading the headings and captions of the tables, you can become aware of what the chapter or article is going to tell you, and focus on the sections that are important for your purpose.

Another convention of scientific writing is that the main point is usually put first. It's not like a murder mystery, where you have to wait for the last page to find out what really happened. In scientific writing, the usual practice is to put the main idea down first, and then to set out the supporting evidence. By reading the little summary at the beginning of an article (the 'abstract') or the summary at the head of a chapter, you can find out what the main thrust of the piece of writing is. So another way to skim is to read the abstract or the first paragraph of the introduction.

READING FOR PREPARATION

The second type of reading you need to do is *preparatory* reading. This is mainly achieved by reading through the relevant sections of your practical manual before you go to a prac class or lab. There may also be references to parts of the main text or to journal articles which contain information relevant to the practical exercise you are about to commence.

Identify the information you need

In many practical classes you are required to write up the experiment as you go along. It can save you a lot of time and puzzlement if you've read material beforehand and sorted out what you need. For example, you may wish to do some preparatory reading on the body temperature control systems of invertebrates; because you have looked at what your experiment entails, you know that you need information about molluscs in particular.

Whatever the reading task, it's important to keep a goal in mind. If you're just letting your eyes drift over the page, from top left to bottom right, with nothing happening in your mind (have you ever read a page and realised at the end of it that nothing went in, that you were thinking about something else altogether?), then your so-called reading time is a waste of time. Whenever you sit down to a reading task, ask yourself these questions:

- Why am I reading this?
- What can I get out of this?
- What is it telling me that is new?
- What does it remind me of?
- What questions does it raise?

The answers to these questions should help you to stay focused on the task. You might like to write down some even more specific questions you need answered. This is a good way to organise and direct your notes: summaries of everything may not be useful. We'll talk a bit more about these ideas in the next section.

READING FOR RESEARCH

The third type of reading you will need to do is *research* reading, where you seek information on a topic for an essay or report. In some science courses there is not much of this sort of writing in the first few semesters, but you will need to do it in later years.

One tricky part of research reading is actually getting it done, as opposed to searching for the books in the library or standing in the queue for the photocopier. You can spend such a lot of time completing these tasks that you feel somehow that you've finished the reading, when you haven't yet done any of it. Don't get sidetracked by 'busy' work.

Previewing can be a real time-saver here; use those skimming techniques to find the material that is most useful for you. In some cases, you might only need to take notes on one or two points; or to photocopy a section rather than a whole article.

A word about the importance of scrupulous research . . .
Of course you need to take full particulars of the source of the information (name of the author, name of the book, date and so on), so that you can properly acknowledge where the information came from, and can find it again; there will be more on using sources in your written assignments in the chapters on writing.

Once you've sorted out and labelled the things you need to read, pause for a few minutes before you start. It's time to remind yourself of your purpose, and to develop some specific research questions. It is wise to keep your essay topic or research question with you all the time. Or you might like to break this main question up into a smaller set of questions. As we said before, these questions can help you focus your reading. Table 6.2 gives some suggestions.

The underlying rule of researching is to stay focused on the task. If you keep your essay question in front of you, and use your specific questions to organise your notes, writing should come more easily. We'll talk a bit more about the process of using your notes for writing essays in Chapter 9.

Table 6.2 Sample questions for research reading

Type of source (examples)	Sample questions
Research article in a journal	What idea was tested? Was the methodology appropriate? Is there a clear conclusion? Are there any flaws in the experiment or argument?
Review article in a journal	Does the writer discuss more than one point of view? What is the writer's conclusion from reviewing the literature? Is the evidence presented fairly? Are there any emotive words used in the argument?
Chapter in textbook	What is the main message? How recent is the evidence? Why is this information important? Are contradictory theories explained clearly?

A word about underlining and highlighting . . .
Some students say they don't like to take notes, they prefer to underline or highlight the important points. BUT highlighting is not the same as understanding, and it is important to be aware of its drawbacks.

It isn't always necessary to take notes when you read, especially if you are reading for context or background. However, note taking is an active learning tool.

If you are reading in order to write, taking notes in your own words is the first step towards writing a draft. When you sit down to write, these notes are far more useful than pages of highlighted text in someone else's words.

If you must highlight, be selective, and write your own comments and questions in the margin.

READING FOR STUDY

The previous chapters on active learning and memorising strategies will have given you an idea about how reading fits into your study schedule. You can review the tables in these chapters to remind yourself of some good strategies. Reading is just *one* study tool.

In fact, although you need to read a great deal of information, you will find it more efficient and more effective to make reading a minor part of your study routine. Of course you need to read the material first: however, endless re-reading will not necessarily help you to remember it. It is too easy to let your eyes physically 'read' while your mind does something much more interesting.

Therefore, reading for study purposes should be an early step in your schedule. You should spend as much time as you can being active with the information—if not physically active, then certainly mentally active as you think about the topics you are studying.

READING EFFECTIVELY AND EFFICIENTLY

What about speed reading?

There are variations in the amount and depth of the reading required for different purposes in your course. Some of you will be wondering whether you should take a 'speed reading' course before you start: if you have the money to spend on that sort of program, you can receive some benefit from it. However, most of your reading will require a level of interaction and analysis (even at the 'Is this important?' stage) that will make speed reading impractical. Efficient reading is better than speed reading for the sophisticated texts you will be dealing with.

Efficient reading includes strategies such as previewing, skimming, and reading with a purpose. It includes techniques such as limiting your reading time to short periods so that you can stay focused on the task and complete the material in sensible sections.

It also includes making efforts to become familiar with the material, because the more you know about anything, the easier it is to learn more. You will find that you are much more efficient when you are comfortable with the way science is written and with the vocabulary of the specific discipline.

New words and how to cope with them

One factor about reading that may be worrying you is the amount of new vocabulary that you are encountering in the texts. You may be tempted to stop at every new word and look it up. There are dangers in this.

One is that when you consult a dictionary (even a dictionary of scientific terms), you cannot always make sense of the sentence in front of you. The context has too great an effect on the meaning.

Another problem is that when you keep stopping to look up words, you lose the thread of the information you are reading. So the time you spend looking up words can mean a big delay in understanding the overall concepts of the material.

A better idea is to collect a few new words (in a special notebook or at the bottom of your page) and then take half an hour to look them up when you don't feel motivated enough to do anything more taxing. That means that when you're reading the text, you just keep reading and many of the words will become clear as you read more about the topic or see the words used in a few different sentences.

If you use your reading time wisely, read from a wide range of sources and read often, you will find that you soon become very familiar with the ideas of your subject. This familiarity will lead to understanding, and that will lead to good marks!

7

NEW
SKILLS

WRITING STYLE

Writing at university level can be more demanding than the writing you have done previously. Sometimes students are discouraged by their sudden inability to write—when it used to be so easy. It's important to recognise that your problem isn't a lack of ability, it's adapting to a new style. The requirements of academic writing may confuse—and annoy—you until you master the conventions.

What is academic writing style?

Just as there are different ways of speaking to different people (you talk to your friends in one speech pattern, and to your employer in another), there are different writing styles. For instance, you probably would not use the same style when writing to your grandmother as when writing to your head of department (unless you have relations in the faculty). Table 7.1 shows examples of different styles and the problems in using these styles for university writing.

Why do I have to write in a specific way?

Scientific style is a global language

Scientific style reflects the aims and ideals of scientific study. As a science student, you are an apprentice researcher: part of your job is to communicate like a scientist. Scientists share factual information with a wide audience, so it is sensible for them to agree on certain principles of writing. Papers from all over the world are written in the same format, with headings, abstracts, and reference lists, so they are easy to access and understand. If you can master the principles of science writing, you will be well on the way to getting excellent marks for your written work.

Scientific style reflects research standards. Scientists adhere strictly to rules about the ownership of work and to the unwritten scientific ethic of complete objectivity. Scientists aim to perform research for information and explanations, without allowing their emotions or biases to interfere with the truth.

SCIENTIFIC STYLE—PRESENT AND FUTURE

These scruples translate into a writing style that may seem cautious, dull, and staid, but is actually accurate and widely readable, once you are familiar with the 'code'. At its best, scientific writing can be assertive, energetic, and enthusing. Because of the requirement that the message is readily understandable, good scientific writing is simple and clear. There's not much room for 'purple prose' in science.

Table 7.1 Good and bad style variations in academic writing

Style	Example	Problems
Colloquial (chatty)—used in speech or an informal letter	'A rough estimate is when you want to check how accurate you're going to be so you put in a few round numbers and see if it's close to what you think it might be so you know if you're going to be right or not.'	Too long and vague; use of personal pronoun ('you') which is too informal; use of contractions ('it's') which is also too informal
Emotive—used to convince others of point of view using feelings	'People are distressed about the ravages occurring daily in the way the state is closing mental health refuges and abandoning mentally ill people to their fate on the streets.'	Use of emotive or dramatic words ('distressed', 'ravages', 'abandoning', 'fate'). Vague reference to 'people': we don't know who is distressed or how many 'people'
Pretentious—used to 'impress' and confuse readers or listeners or to cover ignorance	'It seems probable that the unexpected shift in return could be indicative of perhaps a more wide-ranging phenomenon which may be due to a world-wide change in the economic conditions in countries which, it appears, may have similar contexts.'	Vague and unnecessarily wordy. Too many words which mean 'perhaps': 'seems', 'probable', 'could be', 'perhaps', 'may be', 'appears', 'may have'
Academic—used to convince readers using logic	'This assay is valid (Bradley 1998) when used to calculate how much hormone is released into media in which fragments of anterior pituitary from rats have been incubated.'	No problems! This sentence is precise and sources its information. It has no emotion or bias—we can't tell whether the next sentence will say something positive about the assay or show us its shortcomings
Personalised—used to make personal criticisms or comments about scientific references	'As for child rearing practices, Nguyen and her allies think that traditional methods are unsuccessful, while Khan feels they have importance for the child's emotional development.'	The writer here is making assumptions about what he or she has read—in effect interpreting the sources. You don't know what authors think or feel—you can only work with what they have stated

Scientific style is not static; fashions in writing change just like fashions in anything. The current trend in science is towards the more simple, the more clear, fewer and shorter words. Later in this chapter we will compare some science writing from 30 years ago to some writing from 1996. Looking at examples of scientific writing is a good way to get an idea of what is required—you could go and look at some journals to check this out yourself.

> Joel wonders: 'Last year, I got a lot of good comments about my writing. Especially for taking inventive approaches to my essays. I wrote my Psychology lab report in a way that I thought was interesting and high-lighted the important information, but I got very negative comments for not sticking to the formula. My tutor says there is no place for "different" approaches to writing in this subject . . . It seems pretty boring to me. If they all have to be the same, what's the difference between a good lab report and a bad one?'

ELEMENTS OF GOOD SCIENTIFIC STYLE

The basic rules of scientific writing can be summarised under four major headings: clarity, objectivity, accuracy, and brevity. Table 7.2 shows the main qualities of scientific writing, the dangers, and how to avoid them.

Be clear

You should use ordinary, short, familiar, non-technical terms rather than long, grand, unfamiliar, technical and abstract vocabulary. Naturally, there are specialist terms in your discipline, but don't be unnecessarily pompous. For example, if you are studying meteorology, it is probably fine to write about 'precipitation'. However, if you are writing about the effects of the weather on grazing stock for agricultural science, you should probably talk about 'rain'.

Table 7.2 Scientific style guide

Scientific writing is	Scientific writing is not	How to edit your work for this
Clear	Vague	Avoid unnecessary qualifying words such as rather, seems, almost
Objective	Biased	Check for emotive words, especially adjectives, adverbs, and 'dramatic' verbs
Accurate	Misleading or ambiguous	Avoid equivocal statements and unsupported data; take care with pronouns in long sentences
Concise	Wordy	Check for unnecessary words, double negatives, passive voice, long sentences

If your sentences are very long, you may confuse the reader. It is difficult to control complicated information and relationships in long sentences. It is better to break the material up into more, shorter sentences.

However, you might also confuse your reader by compressing information so much that your sentences become ambiguous. You will have a strict word limit and it's essential to be brief, but you must communicate the information clearly. For example:

The sheep were observed with telescopic lenses.

is a short sentence, but unless this is a report on trained astronomer sheep, it is ambiguous. 'Howlers' like this give markers a laugh during the long hours of correcting papers, but may not earn you many marks. It would be better to write:

The sheep were observed through telescopic lenses.

where attention to just one word has made the meaning perfectly clear. A longer version—in strictly traditional scientific style—would be:

> *Telescopic lenses were used by the researcher to observe the sheep.*

This sentence is written in 'passive voice', which is always longer than its 'active voice' equivalent. In the passive voice, actions are described as being *done by* somebody or something. As in the sentence above, or in this sentence:

> *A number of tests on marshmallow bunnies were performed by the experimenters.*

In the active voice, the person or thing *doing* the action is indicated at the beginning of the sentence. For instance:

> *The experimenters performed a number of tests on the marshmallow bunnies.*

(For further information about these tests, check out 'Bunny Survival Tests Homepage' <http://www.pcola.gulf.net/~irving/bunnies/>. This page is an example of scientific writing style.)

The current trend in scientific writing is towards a shorter, punchier, more active style. If you can be clear using the active voice, that's probably preferable. You don't need to worry about the grammatical terms, as long as you can be clear, complete, and objective. However, if you want to learn more about active and passive voice, or other grammatical terms, there are some good books listed in Appendix I (e.g. Murray-Smith or Day).

Be objective

Scientists must be unbiased, unemotional, and truthful. They use facts, or 'evidence' to convince the reader of the logic of their arguments or how sensible their recommendations are; not emotive language or selective information. Other writers like politicians and advertisers are not bound by such considerations. Their presentation of the facts conveys a biased or 'interested' view.

In your assignments, you should be putting across a point of view (you can call this a 'position' or 'argument'), but you must also show that you are aware of other different or opposing outlooks. You must show evidence to support your point of view; and account for alternative views. Try to present a balanced viewpoint.

How do I know if something is biased?

In the last chapter we talked about reading critically. This can be important in your writing. Here's an example. You are writing a report on the practice of docking dogs' tails, and you come across an article written by a poodle breeder in Switzerland—where docking is banned—who claims that in the first year of the new law there has been a 25 per cent increase in the number of tail injuries. This looks bad for your point of view, that docking should be banned. However, when you look at the actual figures and find out that this '25 per cent' is based on four cases of tail injury one year and five the next . . . the breeder's 'facts' no longer look so convincing.

When you write, don't try to trick people into believing what you say. It's better to present an opinion that acknowledges some room for doubt or opposing ideas.

Let's have a look at another example, this time a superficially factual piece which in fact contains a clear bias:

The tiny marsupial numbat, the only living Myrmecobiidae, with its bottlebrush-like stripes and delicate face, its young clinging to its back, is fast losing its remaining habitat in diminishing pockets of eucalypt forest.

The writer is trying to make the reader feel sorry for the numbats. We can tell this by the use of descriptive words such as 'tiny' and 'delicate', by comparisons with flowers ('bottlebrush-like'), and by the use of dramatic words such as 'clinging', 'diminishing', and 'pockets'. Although the style of writing looks quite straightforward, the vocabulary allows the writer's bias to show. This information can be written more objectively:

> *The loss of eucalypt forests is reducing the habitat of the last Myrmecobiidae species, the marsupial numbat, which carries its young on its back.*

As you can see, the second version is not only more objective, but shorter. Much more scientific!

Be accurate

Your piece of scientific writing will contain facts and it is expected that those facts will be accurate and complete. There is no room for vague, ambiguous, or misleading statements in science. If in doubt, check a reliable source. Some pointers to remember are:

- Only use information for which you have good evidence—not that your friend's cousin went to Central Australia and told you about the seven different colours that can be seen in the face of Uluru; if you want to discuss the strata you need to consult a geological report.
- Be consistent in your use of units of measurement so that the reader can make comparisons easily. If you write *'The bacteria decreased by one-third after the first treatment but there was a 12% decrease after the second'* you are making it very hard for your reader to follow.
- Acknowledge where your data are incomplete and give a fair appraisal of how important your figures are; if your study sample was too small for any powerful statistical analysis, be frank about it. If few or no conclusions can be drawn, say so.

- Check and recheck the illustrations to make sure that the data contained are correct. The same goes for calculations. Small mistakes can lead to big embarrassments as well as being misleading.
- Your department will give you information about scientific conventions for important details like referencing style and standard abbreviations. Don't be tempted to make up your own!

Be brief

The word limits attached to assignments can be positively stingy. Yet whether you are preparing a 400-word lab report or a 15 000-word essay, there is no room for unnecessary information or repetition. Every one of those 400 or 15 000 words must count.

One way to cope with this is to think of your limited words as so many dollars. If you only have $400 to spend, is it worth wasting money on repetitions or padding at $1 per word? Perhaps you will write many more than the word limit on your first draft (yes! you will often need to draft assignments), but you need to develop your editing skills so that only the best 400 words of what you have written are submitted. Editing means learning how to cut.

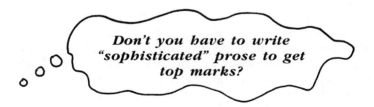

Don't you have to write "sophisticated" prose to get top marks?

You can help yourself by using precise terms to say exactly what you mean. Sometimes students feel that their language has to be complicated to be good. This is not true. Lecturers aren't impressed by fancy language. Always try to write what you mean, not something that 'sounds impressive'.

Sometimes the best science writing involves 'translation' from a formal sentence into a more readily understood everyday one. For example:

We do not know which technique is most efficient.

is better than:

At the time of writing, there is a persistent obfuscation of the eventual preference assumed with regard to the emergence of the desired technique in relation to the maximum efficiency of outcome.

PERSONAL PRONOUNS—WHERE OBJECTIVITY AND BREVITY COLLIDE

Zoe has found a contradiction: 'One of my lecturers said never to say "I" when you are writing. But another one said my essay introduction needed a sentence which stated: "In this essay, I will argue . . ." I'm confused. Is it okay or not?'

Note that some departments and lecturers dislike the use of personal pronouns (e.g. using 'we' or 'I'). This is because of the scientific emphasis on objectivity. Editors of scientific journals—and some of the people marking your assignments—fear that if you say 'we' or 'I', you are dangerously close to becoming personally involved with the data.

Recently, some disciplines of science have been relaxing their rules about personal pronouns, and now prefer using the 'we performed . . .' style sentence (shorter, active voice) to the 'the experiment was performed by . . .' style (longer, passive voice). The two passages below show the changes in style over time.

A new method for removal of the brain is described. This

is intended to stress the relation of the brain and the cranial nerves to the meninges, and should help to make a closer link between the study of the head and neck and brain than is possible when the brain is removed in a single operation. An alternative dissection for the removal of the brain is described for those departments where it is necessary to use the brain from the cadaver for more detailed study.

from G. J. Romanes, *Cunningham's Manual of Practical Anatomy: Volume 3, Head and Neck and Brain*, thirteenth edition, Oxford University Press, 1966, p. vii.

Not all information systems use application controls to the same degree, nor do they all need to. Much depends on the nature of the application and how critical its data are. We can expect major banking and financial systems to use more controls than other systems because so much money and credibility is at stake.

from K. C. Laudon and J. Price Laudon, *Information Systems: A problem-solving approach*, third edition, Dryden Press, 1995, p. 450.

A COUPLE OF COMMON WRITING PROBLEMS

The emphasis on objectivity sometimes makes departments discourage the use of the active voice. However, the active voice is the shorter version. Your departmental guidelines will advise you about this. When you can use the active voice without compromising objectivity, do so.

Don't waste words repeating ideas. Are you tempted to use many words when one will do? You may think it makes your paper sound better, but vague waffling will be recognised and won't earn you marks. Use the relevant vocabulary for your area, but don't be pompous just because you are writing a formal assignment. Keep it short and use the simplest word possible. Look at these examples:

Table 7.3 Tautological phrases

in view of the foregoing circumstances	= therefore
are found to be in agreement	= agree
afford an opportunity to investigate	= allow investigation

Verbosity is usually an attempt to make a little information go a long way. Markers want clear writing, not otiose, lexiphanic parisology. Table 7.4 summarises the pitfalls of pompous, overly formal writing.

Table 7.4 What you should avoid

Writing type	Example	Use instead
Double negatives	not unlikely, not unknown	likely, known
Tautology (repetition of ideas)	advance forward, exact duplicate, singularly unique	advance, duplicate (or 'copy'), unique
Unnecessary jargon	annual precipitation statistic	mean annual rainfall

EDITING POINTERS FOR GOOD SCIENTIFIC WRITING

Your best guide to scientific writing is to make your message as clear as it can be. You should not allow any possibility of misunderstanding. If you have the chance to draft and redraft, then do it. If you're writing up a report in a lab as you do the practical exercise, then keep your sentences simple and short.

You should also develop your editing skills. The examples and qualities outlined above show you what to look for. Identify any typical failings (for example, writing long sentences all the time), and edit for them. If you are inclined to be biased (for example, you always take a conservationist or a rural industries slant in agricultural essays), then look carefully for emotive words and make sure you have presented alternatives fairly.

To develop your own familiarity with scientific writing style, you need practice. You won't master it at the first attempt. But you will master it! It's a matter of playing by the rules in order to score points. Practise, practise, practise.

The next chapters will show you how to approach writing specific science assignments such as laboratory reports and essays, and how to edit your work to get the best marks for your efforts.

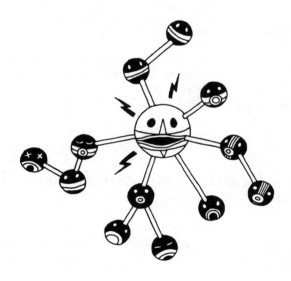

SPECIFIC WRITING REQUIREMENTS

WRITING LABORATORY REPORTS

Lab reports are a written version of the experiment or exercise that you performed in the lab or practical class. Each department has its own preferred structure for lab reports, but there is a general format that they all conform to. This structure is part of the scientific style we described in the last chapter.

Why do we have to write up our labs?

Writing lab reports is in fact the start of becoming a professional scientist. Most articles in scientific journals are based on the laboratory report structure. Here, we'll present some basic guidelines for report writing. *If your departmental guide is different, then follow it.*

For your first few reports you may only be required to write up one or two sections of the lab—e.g. introduction and results.

HEADINGS

A laboratory report may include:

Title
Abstract
~ Introduction
~ Materials and Methods
~ Results
Discussion
Conclusion
Acknowledgments
References
Appendices

Not all of these sections are used in all departments or at all year levels.

Articles in scientific journals—especially those which report the results of experiments or tests—follow a similar format. This is sometimes referred to as the 'IMRAD' format: introduction, methods, results, analysis, discussion. The introductory section makes a claim that is supported or demonstrated by the evidence in later sections. Evidence presented is drawn together in a concluding section.

TITLE AND THE TITLE PAGE

The lab report title may be set by the department and appear in your handbook or prac manual, so check there first. If you have to make up your own title, make it brief, informative, and interesting. It is not usually a sentence. If your title is too brief, for example—'Seed Yield', or 'Dye Patterns'—it will be too general to be informative and interesting. On the other hand, more than twelve words is probably too many. Be concise and meaningful: not 'Enzymes in Bacteria', but 'Dihydrofolate Reductase in *Baccillus subtilis*'.

Your name, your student number, the date of the experiment, the demonstrator's name, the due date and the title of the experiment are all included on the title page. You may need to fill in a form and put it on the front of your report. Don't forget this important information.

ABSTRACT

This can be the most difficult part of the laboratory report to write. It must be short—often less than 100 words—and certainly not more than 5 per cent of the total wordage. Most abstracts are a single paragraph. The abstract must make complete sense on its own. Don't repeat the title in the abstract, but state the aims of the experiment, the results reached, and the methods used. Conclude with the principal findings. Remember, the abstract summarises the *whole* report.

As you may have guessed, it is best to write the abstract after everything else, so that you know exactly what your findings and conclusions are! There are not usually references in abstracts (more about references later).

INTRODUCTION

Your introduction should be clear and concise. It tells the reader what to expect in your report. Table 8.1 summarises the four important ingredients in any good introduction.

The introduction is written in the past tense, and in scientific style (see Chapter 7). Like abstracts, introductions are often written after the other sections.

Table 8.1 The elements of an introduction

Problem	State the area investigated by the experiment
Background	Summarise previous research in the area, narrow the area of study
Objectives	Give the aim of your experiment and state the method
Hypothesis	State this clearly (it may be in your laboratory manual, so check there first)

MATERIALS AND METHODS

Sometimes this section has subheadings such as Subjects, Apparatus, Procedure. This section should contain clear enough instructions for someone to be able to replicate your experiment. If in doubt, that's the guideline to use. You describe the experimental design, the treatments, the apparatus, and the subjects. This section is easy—you know what you did.

There are rules for the conventional descriptions of chemicals, animals, and plants. Follow these exactly as recommended by your department. For example, common names of animals or plants are only acceptable if they are followed by scientific description in brackets after the first such use; e.g. 'the sooty shearwater (*Puffinus griseus*)'.

In general, do not use trade names for chemicals; use instead the generic or chemical names. You may use standard, well-known abbreviations (such as NaCl), but do not make your paper too difficult to follow by overuse of these (it is usual to write 'water' rather than 'H_2O').

If you have made any of the apparatus yourself, you must explain it clearly, and perhaps show its construction in a diagram. Standard apparatus should be described in proper technical terms; i.e., not 'a big test tube', but 'a test tube of 13.5 cm diameter'. Technical terms can be appropriate in this context.

When reporting field experiments, it is usual to describe the soil type, and the weather, which may have been an important factor.

> Zoe says: 'I got an okay mark for my first Zoology lab report, but I was told my report was much too long. My demonstrator said my method section had way too much information.
>
> 'I thought you had to say what you did so that someone could copy your lab exactly, but my demonstrator crossed out huge chunks of my work. He said you don't need to explain things like the format for recording raw data or detailed descriptions of equipment.
>
> 'Also, he said it can be okay to refer to other books or experiments for description of complicated but common procedures.
>
> 'I guess I made a mistake in assuming my report was written for someone who didn't know the subject. If I think about writing for someone in my class I find it easier to decide what to put in.'

Describe your procedures and methods of measurement (use past tense). Sometimes (where standard procedures are used) you can cite a reference rather than giving a particular procedure; e.g., 'as in O'Toole's (1994) paper'. However, do not simply say 'as in the Physics 1M manual'; you must practise using your own words to describe your actions— unless your demonstrator tells you otherwise.

At the end of the materials and methods section, you should also give details of how you analysed data. Long statistical calculations can be attached in an appendix; we'll explain appendices a bit more later.

RESULTS

This is a simple section, because it merely describes what happened. Yet in terms of scientific value, it is the most important section of your paper. Here you report the data upon which you have based your conclusions. Accuracy and clarity are of prime importance here. The reader can quarrel with your interpretations, but there should be no areas of dispute in your results. Some students like the fact that results are so clearly right or wrong, while others find them difficult, for that reason.

Simple errors here are as easy to spot as they are to make, so check that you have accurately and faithfully reported the results of your experiment. If the results look vague or sloppy, your marker imagines that is the sort of scientist you are!

Report first the results bearing directly on the title of your laboratory report. Any other interesting findings come after this. If you had more than one hypothesis, you may want to organise your results to reflect this.

Never falsify findings; if your results did not support the hypothesis, no matter how well accepted that hypothesis, then say so. (However, all such explanation belongs in the discussion section, not with the results.) If, in your experiment, gravity forced objects away from the Earth, or every chicken turned away from light, then report that fact. There will no doubt be good reasons for these happenings, and it is up to you, as the scientist, to put forward (in the discussion section) possible explanations (such as faulty methodology, or the discovery of a new strain of nocturnal-feeding poultry).

Don't be disappointed by negative results. You have still discovered something: even if you are only adding to a process of elimination, you are contributing to scientific endeavour. A negative result is still a result.

TABLES AND FIGURES

Do I have to put in diagrams and stuff?

Results are often given in the forms of tables and figures. There are certain ways to do this. Figures and tables do not simply repeat information given in the text; they summarise, amplify, or complement it. Tables and figures are most common in the results section, but the rules for presentation are the same no matter which section they appear in.

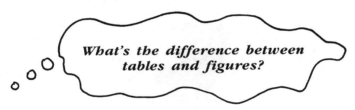

What's the difference between tables and figures?

Tables usually present data in columns of numbers, or values. Tables are given a caption at the top, and numbered as they appear—Table 1, and so on. You should mention each table in the written part (text) of the Results section, usually just pointing out the most important cell. For example, 'The effect of the fertiliser was greatest in the northern plot, as shown in Table 3.' It is also fine to put the reference to the table or figure in brackets at the end of a sentence (Table 2).

The other type of 'illustration' you can use in a lab report is a figure. A figure can be lots of different things. Figures include diagrams, graphs, drawings, photos—in fact anything that's not a table. Figures are numbered separately from tables, so you have Table 1 and also Figure 1.

Figures are also captioned, but their captions appear below the figure. You should also write about each figure in the text. As you can see, when you write about the illustrations, you use capital letters for each Figure and Table.

Some examples are below.

Table 1 Quality of cat purrs for sample period 1 (120s)

Breed	Vibrations	Respirations	Volume(db)	Duration
Russian Blue	700	47	63	120
Siamese	674	50	59	120
Non-pedigree	745	48	60	100
Chinchilla	596	51	57	46
Maine Coon	710	46	66	120

Figure 1 An image from the DOGZ program

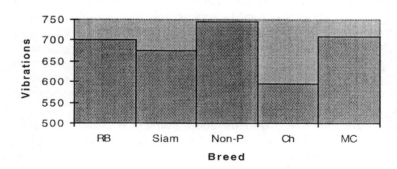

Figure 2 Purr vibrations by breed

Figure 2 presents some information from Table 1 in a new form. Generally, you can present information in a table or a figure, but not both. Sometimes you will be told which format to use, or you might have to decide for yourself. Pick the format that shows the relevant results the most clearly.

DISCUSSION

A lot of students find this section the most troublesome to write. That's because it requires the most thinking. In the discussion, you comment on the results you have reported in the previous section.

The discussion has clear connections with the introduction; these connections may include subheadings or organisation. Sometimes it is easiest to write about the results by breaking your discussion into subsections, especially if there was a multifactorial design. (You should be using the past tense in all these sections.)

In the discussion, you should analyse the results, and link your results with what you read in the text, prac manual, or other sources that you talked about in the introduction. You say whether or not the results supported the hypothesis; if not, this is where you can suggest reasons why. Were there any general trends that became obvious? This is also where you may comment on suspect methodology or reliability—that is, where you talk about what you did wrong in terms of design and procedures.

You then have a concluding paragraph (it may be as little as one sentence) that states the significance of your findings, and perhaps suggests further steps in the scientific process. For example, you may state that it would be advisable to repeat the experiment with corrections to the procedures, or that a future researcher could discover more by adding an extra dimension to your design.

ACKNOWLEDGMENTS

It is courteous to acknowledge any special help. This is regularly done at the end of a paper or thesis, but not usually in a lab report. You will see acknowledgments at the end of articles in scientific journals.

REFERENCES

Here's a brief word about citation—there's more detail in the next chapter.

You will consult different 'sources' of information (textbooks, journals, lab manuals, Internet etc.) when you need something to put into your introduction. At university level, you must tell the reader where you found any information that is not common knowledge and that you didn't spontaneously think of yourself.

Any time you write in your assignment a piece of information that you collected from a source, you will need to cite that source. All the sources you 'cite' are called 'references'.

At the end of your laboratory report, you will need to attach a list of references. This list must contain everything you cited in the report, and nothing more. If you read it, but didn't cite, it doesn't (normally) go in your list. The exception here is when you are asked to provide a *bibliography*, rather than a reference list. A bibliography is a list of everything you read, whether you cite it or not.

There are specific citation and referencing conventions used in scientific disciplines and there will either be a guide to these published by your department, or your department might recommend a style in a specific journal (like *Evolution* for Genetics) or manual (like the *APA Style Manual* for Psychology).

APPENDICES

You don't have to have an appendix or appendices in your report, but there might be some detailed information that you want to include. For instance, an appendix might contain the raw data for your results—results sections are a summary of findings, so the initial unprocessed figures don't really belong there.

Appendices may also include information from the method section: samples of questionnaires used, proof of ethics approval, survey map of the area where you did your fieldwork.

Appendices are numbered, and each appendix needs a heading with its number clearly indicated. In the text when you want the reader to know where he/she can find more detailed information, you need to refer to the appendix by number as you do for tables and figures. This reference often comes in brackets at the end of a sentence: (see Appendix 3).

PRESENTATION

Before submitting your laboratory report, check it for spelling, grammar, and layout, as well as making sure the content is correct (or as close as you can make it!). It's a good idea to check whether you need to type your report, and whether hand-drawn graphs are okay. Your department might prefer centred headings, or 4 cm margins right and left, or double spacing, so it's important to get it right. Why waste marks on simple format details?

In general, science departments don't go in for anything fancy, so don't be tempted to hand in green headings and purple underlinings, or coloured paper. Correct any errors. Then hand it in on time!

SPECIFIC WRITING REQUIREMENTS

SCIENTIFIC ESSAYS

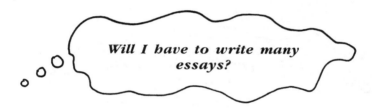

Will I have to write many essays?

Essays are not usually a major focus of assessment in science courses. You may not write essays until second year or later. Because they are rare, essays can be a daunting prospect. This guide gives you the basics.

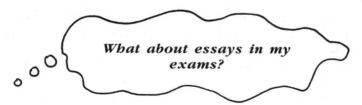

What about essays in my exams?

Sometimes the first essay you write for the year is during the exams. If this is going to happen in your course, read this chapter and the one on exams in science, because some of this advice will be useful.

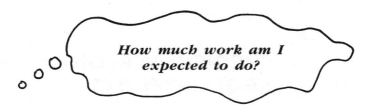

How much work am I expected to do?

Essay writing can be broken into a number of steps, and if you follow them through, put in a reasonable amount of time and allow yourself at least two drafts, you'll be fine. The basic steps are choosing and planning an approach to your research, reading, planning your essay, writing the various elements, and editing your work. We'll explain them in more detail later.

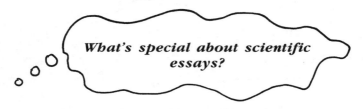

What's special about scientific essays?

Your major tasks in writing a scientific essay are to:

- demonstrate a thorough understanding of the topic area through your reading;
- review the relevant literature, explaining different perspectives of the problem and giving a critical examination of the material you have read;
- present the relevant data in an accurate, unbiased and factual manner;
- discuss the major contradictory view with reasons for why it is less acceptable than the one you are advocating;
- demonstrate good written expression, including spelling, punctuation and grammar;
- show where you have found the information, with accurate and thorough citation and referencing.

GENERAL GUIDELINES

A scientific essay is different from a lab report. You will investigate a topic and write a coherent text about it, in a set word limit of anything from 400 words up.

Where does the information come from?

Investigating the topic means finding—and then reading—the relevant literature. You incorporate information from these sources (books and journal articles) to form an argument. You may think at the outset that there is only one way of looking at a particular topic, but the more you read, the more you learn about it. There are few, if any, absolute answers. You are looking for the most plausible argument from the evidence you find in your sources.

There are identifiable sections in a scientific essay, but not necessarily headings for each section, though headings and illustrations (see Chapter 8) are more common in a scientific essay than a humanities one.

The basic structure of the scientific essay is introduction, exposition, and conclusion. The introduction tells us what you are going to 'argue'; the exposition shows us the evidence that led you to that point of view (make sure that it is not simply a description of the topic); the conclusion summarises the argument.

Remember, scientific essays require a definite statement of your argument ('thesis'/'proposition') in the introduction. Then you prove that idea in the main body of the essay, and conclude by saying that the evidence you have discussed supports it. Let your reader know what's happening.

You do not save any important information to surprise the reader in the conclusion, and you are not writing a mystery so you do not sprinkle red herrings (misleading facts or arguments) throughout the essay.

Evidence is important in any essay at tertiary level; it is not appropriate to make stuff up. However, you also need to express an opinion. You may agree or disagree with the essay question/proposition. Sometimes because there are still so many unknowns in science, you might be less sure about the answer. It's okay to say 'in these particular instances, yes; but in these others, no'. You still need to make it clear when the 'yes' and the 'no' apply. This doesn't mean you can take the easy way out by not committing yourself: *you must have a definite answer;* even if it is qualified (that is, not the total solution to the problem).

For example:

YES: 'The spontaneous creation of cell hybrids formed by the fusion of somatic cells was the most important precursor of the present science of somatic cell genetics.'

NO: 'The statistical approach to texture classification and segmentation pioneered by Laws (1980) has shortcomings when used to capture all texture features of natural images.'

QUALIFIED YES AND NO: 'While elementary functions of the body have a precise location in particular cortical cells, the location of complex functional systems in limited areas of brain tissue is not possible.'

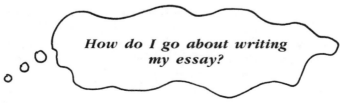

How do I go about writing my essay?

You will find it easier to write your essay if you break it down into separate tasks (remember, achievable goals!) and follow these steps.

MEET YOUR TOPIC

Sometimes you get to choose the topic; at other times it will be set. If you have questions to choose from, read them all carefully. Sometimes questions that look easy on the surface are actually quite complicated. Pay attention to what the question is actually asking, don't just grab a topic area and start writing.

Don't get too clever if you're allowed to write your own topic: the course has set goals and what you think is related may be a bit off track and cost you marks. You need a very clear idea of what your topic is—exactly—before you start research.

Explore your topic. Writing an essay is an opportunity to find out more about something. It's okay to choose a topic you don't know much about—by the time you have written your essay, you'll be an expert.

Spend fifteen minutes or so 'brainstorming' your topic. Write the topic on a piece of paper, and then write down all the ideas and questions you have about it. You can brainstorm with a friend if you like. The purpose of this mental task is to familiarise you with the key terms, and work out some research questions to help focus your reading.

RESEARCH THE TOPIC

You will have a starting list of references, but you should do further reading. Chapter 6 has help on approaching this task. It's a good sign if you first become very enthused about your topic and start explaining it to every hapless bystander, and then later become *confused* about it as you read more widely and realise that there are lots of apparently valid but contrasting viewpoints.

> Joel had a problem: 'My essay questions for Psychology and Sociology were practically the same, they were both about group processes. I handed the Sociology essay in first, and I got quite a good mark. But I failed my Psych essay. I don't really understand why. My Psych tutor said my references weren't appropriate for Psychology, even though they were okay for my other essay.'

The information you use needs to be appropriate for the subject you are working in. As Joel's experience shows, information that is seen as legitimate in one subject may be irrelevant in another. Always keep in mind the subject matter and the audience of your essay. You should concentrate on biology evidence for Biol essays, and so on. If you start your research from the recommended readings, you will be heading in the right direction. Once you have done the reading set by your lecturer, you may want to expand your avenues for research. This could be a good time to look on the Web, or at other types of sources.

SET A RESEARCH DEADLINE

It's wise to set a limit to your information collection time, or you may become overwhelmed and leave yourself no time to write. Remember you're not writing a novel and you have a time limit. You're expected to look at enough literature to gain a good insight into the topic and to appreciate the complexities of it: too little reading, and your essay will show only a superficial understanding of the task. Too much and you'll write a thesis and not get it handed in until the year 2050.

How many books and articles should I read?

Sometimes you will be told how many references to use. If not, a practical guideline is to research about 10–15 times the number of words that you have to write. For a 2000 word essay, that means reading about 10–15 sources of about the same length as your essay (8–10 pages), or fewer longer sources.

PLAN YOUR ESSAY STRUCTURE—A MATTER OF ARGUMENT

Of course you need an introduction, a main body, and a conclusion. You have a couple of options: don't worry about the introduction until you know what you're going to write; or write a draft introduction which is basically an essay outline. Leave the conclusion until later. The focus of your plan is the body of the essay.

To do this, you need a fair idea of what you're going to 'argue' or propose in the essay. Your reading should give you some point of view on the topic, or you may start with some idea of what you think about it.

Sam agrees with the major theories —

Joel thinks the woman with the off-beat approach is on a winner—

Zoe would really like to see them all remembering the practicalities and making them fit into their theories—

and the authors of this book think that if this element of that idea were to be combined with this element of the other as well as a bit of what the first author said . . .

As you can see, your 'argument', or best solution, or proposition, or insight, or 'thesis' is not as simple as 'this reference is the correct answer'. Which leads us to an important point—your essay exists inside your head as much as in any references in the library.

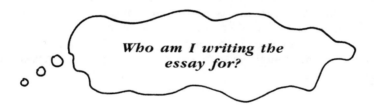

Who am I writing the essay for?

Think of the reader as someone in your year—intelligent and able to understand complex ideas, but who hasn't read much in this topic. One of the first things you need to explain to this person is the specific vocabulary of the area. You must define your terms, but this doesn't mean define every word. As a rule of thumb, you should define unusual or specific vocabulary, common words that have special meanings in this context, and terms that are disputed in the literature. Use a working definition extracted from reading the work of experts in the area (not from the dictionary).

Then think about what you need to explain to this person about current thinking in the area. Maybe you'll go through a short history of work in the area or perhaps explain the views of the major theorists.

Basically, you can structure your argument in three ways: agree with the main proposition in the question, disagree, or agree to a limited extent. Your essay is usually structured with an explanation of your view, then the evidence for your view and against other interpretations.

WRITE UP THE SEPARATE POINTS

You need to work the information you have gathered into sensible paragraphs, each of which performs a function. For example, you will probably have a paragraph explaining each of the major theories. You'll have a paragraph defining your terms. You'll have paragraphs giving examples of how the theories apply in practice. You'll have paragraphs elaborating the occasions when something different happens. You'll have paragraphs showing how what you've read doesn't apply to specific data/problems/situations.

LINK THE PARTS OF THE ESSAY

To make a coherent argument, you must fuse all this information into one logical, readable text. Usually this means the addition of 'continuation' sentences to your paragraphs. Another useful device is the creation of summing-up and introductory paragraphs to sit between the different sections of the essay. Work out some links between the major ideas of your essay.

Sometimes students worry that linking passages are repetitive. Well, sometimes they are, because it's difficult to think of new ways to express similar concepts. However, you need to remember your reader. He or she hasn't been working on the topic for three weeks, and may not be able to follow the logic of your argument without guidance.

Your paragraphs should be built around a topic sentence—in science, the first sentence of the paragraph—and each paragraph should elaborate on a single idea. However, each paragraph should be clearly related to those around it, so you'll need continuation words (such as 'however', 'in addition', 'also' etc.) or sentences to make it all work together.

WRITE THE CONCLUSION

Going through all this should clarify your ideas. Actually, it helps you to understand something if you have to express it in words, either written or spoken. So you should be able to sum up well.

The conclusion should have no surprises for either the reader or you. It should be a satisfying tying together of your points so that the main argument of the essay is unambiguously stated. Don't introduce new material and don't finish with a quote—all that work just so you could reach someone else's proposition?

WRITE THE INTRODUCTION

Academic essays have peculiar introductions. You must say what you're going to argue before you present the evidence. The introduction has four main elements, as in lab reports: in an essay you state the topic (not in the very same words as the question), the background, the focus of your essay (how you're going to approach the topic), and what your 'hypothesis' or main idea about the topic is.

PREPARING TO EDIT YOUR DRAFT

Once you've written the first draft, you should try to leave it alone for a day or two. It's very difficult to edit your own work.

If you leave it for a little, you can look at it with fresh eyes. This means you need to plan time for revisions. You might like to ask someone else to read the essay during this time.

Ideally you should write several drafts of your essay, and there are specific elements you need to change at each drafting stage. If you think about it, it makes more sense to change the structure first, and then worry about the expression. Agonising over the perfect sentence is a waste of time if you end up deleting the paragraph it was in. Table 9.1 presents some editing tips.

GENERAL GUIDELINES FOR CITATION

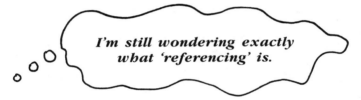

At tertiary level, you need to be careful about stating clearly where you got your information. Universities are places where the highest level of thinking is encouraged and people are rewarded for the quality of their thoughts. Their thoughts are their 'handiwork'; their intellectual property. Researchers and theorists own their thoughts and writings. They are rewarded for the quality of these with research posts and teaching positions, industry research grants and government advisory jobs. If they steal one another's ideas (this is called 'plagiarism'), they could steal one another's livelihood. You need to respect other people's ideas.

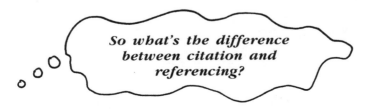

Table 9.1 Editing strategies

Editing task	Who does it?	Looking for …	Strategies	Questions to ask
Changes to structure	You	Clear argument, order of points, length, use of sources	Compare to your plan, research questions or to the essay question	Are there links? Are the connections clear? Is it balanced? Do I need more references, or fewer?
Improving expression	You, maybe with help	Structure of paragraphs, coherent sentences, active voice, no waffling, good referencing	Read it from the marker's perspective, read it aloud, get help, read just your topic sentences to check linking	Have I said everything? Does the argument flow? Have I cut unnecessary words? Are my sentences clear?
Proofreading	Preferably someone else	Details, spelling, punctuation, grammar, references	Someone else can probably see errors you don't, leave it for a while, read aloud, read it backwards, print it out	Is the grammar correct and clear? Are the pages numbered? Any spelling mistakes? Any problems?

What does this mean to you as a student? It means that you need to acknowledge the sources of your information. You must tell us where you found the data you used in your essay. This is when you 'cite' the 'reference' which was the source of the information. A web site that is a good starting point for referencing styles is <http://www.ddce.cqu.edu.au/refandcitation/home.htm>.

Failure to provide adequate citation will be 'plagiarism' and is usually given a zero mark without the chance to resubmit the work. You may even be reported and/or disciplined. If that sounds scary, it's meant to. Universities take plagiarism very seriously.

There are two types of plagiarism.

Plagiarism occurs when you use others' ideas without acknowledgment, or when you use someone else's words—even with acknowledgment—without direct quotation marks.

You will not get good marks for your essay if you simply gather complete sentences from your sources, cite the authors, and join the whole together to form your essay. This could be done by any reasonably intelligent trained poodle: your marker is looking for evidence that you have critically analysed what you have read, not merely copied it.

USE READING MATERIAL WISELY

You may think that you can write your essay without looking at sources: this will result in a failed essay as well. Remember that part of your task is to find out the background of the topic and the current state of research. That is why it is important to read in the academic journals, for this is where the most recent publications are.

> Zoe says: 'I can find lots of information for my essay topic on the internet, and I wanted to know if it is okay to use it. My demonstrator said that this internet information is not always as highly regarded as information in refereed journals.'

What about the "information superhighway"?

You must be very careful about information from internet sources. There are some very good sources of information online, especially in academic newsgroups or online journals. But don't think something a friend told you in IRC (Internet Relay Chat) is a recognised scientific source. Like printed matter, internet material must be referenced properly. If your style guide doesn't mention the 'net, there are plenty of style sheets available online to help you (see Appendix III).

How should you proceed through this complicated pathway to referencing? First, always keep track of where the information came from; second, take notes in your own words *or* put quotation marks around sentences you copy directly from the text. Then use the citation style recommended by your department. No problems!

If you are still in the dark, we have included a reference list in Appendix I at the back of this book, which lists a number of reputable style guides.

I failed! What went wrong?

It's very disheartening when you put in a huge effort, and then get a terrible mark. Most of the time, good marks for essays are about fulfilling the requirements. (The following list is meant to help you pass, not scare you.)

The main reasons for failing scientific essays are:

- failure to present a clear argument;
- lack of sound evidence to support the argument;
- emphasis on description rather than evaluation;
- overuse of out-of-date information;
- failure to refute possible alternative arguments;
- poor logical structure;
- inappropriate style;
- poor introduction and/or conclusion;
- poor presentation;
- lack of or poor citation;
- plagiarism.

10 PREPARING FOR YOUR EXAMS

One of the most daunting features of studying science at university level is facing the exams at the end of semester. This is because the bulk of your assessment—from 80 to 100 per cent—is usually by examination. For students accustomed to continuous assessment, this can cause great anxiety.

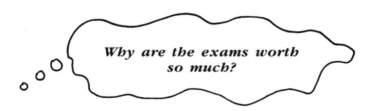

Why are the exams worth so much?

There are many reasons given both for and against assessment by examination: let's just say that it's an effective way to assess many students at the same time, and that exam pressure mimics stresses which occur in responsible jobs such as those aspired to by many science students. Whichever way you look at them, exams are here to stay, and you must learn to succeed in them.

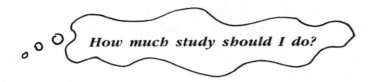

How much study should I do?

You therefore need to prepare very well for exams. If you think about putting in effort in proportion to the marks that your assessment tasks are worth, you will get an idea of how much exam study is appropriate. Unlike in Year 12, when exam study was something you did at the end of the year or semester, exam study at uni should start very early. Lots of the things you do—like reading for preparation, or doing tute sheets—are also exam prep. You can also start to do a little regular weekly revision after the first week of semester.

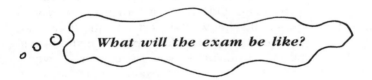

What will the exam be like?

In most science disciplines you will face a variety of examination formats. The most common are multiple choice exams, problem solving exams, short answer exams, essay exams, and practical exams.

MULTIPLE CHOICE EXAMS

Even the multiple choice format can be divided into question types. There are those that ask you to identify the answer that doesn't fit; there are true/false questions; there are questions that give you a hypothetical situation and ask you to apply principles that you have studied; and there are also multiple choice questions that ask you to extend the information according to the theories that you have learned.

Multiple choice is not just multiple guess. The important thing to remember is that there are very few multiple choice questions at university level that require you simply to recognise the right answer. You are expected to combine pieces of information from lectures throughout the semester, to understand a new sequence based on something you have met in another shape, and to apply principles to new situations. It's not that you'll never get another 'recognise the most familiar one' question: just that these will be limited.

This means that you need to prepare for exams earlier than you think, because you will do so much better with a bit of understanding than with a mere parrot-like recognition of facts. Remember what we said about levels of knowledge in Chapters 2 and 4? You might think you only need level 1, but it may not be enough.

Get familiar with the format. When you have a multiple choice test approaching, find out what format the questions will take. You should know the sort of questions, the weighting of the questions, and the response method—will you have to fill in a card, or do you circle your answers?

Sometimes you can look at old exam papers (at some universities, they are available on the 'net), and this will help you as long as you use them sensibly. That means practising all or part of the exam under exam conditions—no music, coffee, comfortable chair or textbook open at the appropriate page—so that you can find out what you really don't know. After you have done them, these practice exams can also be useful study tools.

PROBLEM SOLVING EXAMS

Problem solving exams are common in the science disciplines. These should be the easiest exams because you have been solving problems all semester. (At least, you should have been!)

Usually you will have a weekly tutorial sheet of problems which you work through at home or with the tutor during classes. Sometimes problems are demonstrated in lectures. It is important that you stay up to date with these examples of problem solving so that your own expertise increases over the semester. Regular practice is the best study method.

Frequent practice at solving problems is an excellent way to prepare for these exams; so if you have been keeping up with your tute sheets, you have also been preparing for your exam. If you haven't been in the habit before, you can see why you will need regular sessions wrestling with the tute sheets every week. Many students hate problems, often for different reasons—they can't get started, or they get halfway and get lost, or they just can't solve the last line.

A good way around this is to work regularly with a group of fellow students. Perhaps one of you is very good at seeing how to start the problem, while another is good at tying up the finish. Together you can learn from each other how to tackle these problems for the benefit of all.

A word about collaborative learning . . .
Science students can be very competitive, especially when they're looking at quota subjects or at getting into a specialist course. It is a mistake to let this competition prevent you all from gaining the maximum benefit from working alongside other clever people. Also, working with others helps you get different perspectives on questions, which helps you to understand concepts. And, after all, working with a team is what you'll be doing when you're a qualified scientist.

To prepare for problem solving exams, it's therefore good to join or initiate a problem solving group. Even talking problems over with others so you can compare answers and approaches will be helpful. Revise old tutorial sheets actively—that is, making sure you know how each problem can be solved and proving it to yourself perhaps by substituting different values and reworking them. Try to do the same task in a different context.

Another beneficial exercise is to try to understand how the formulae you are using work. What is each element there for? How does each manipulate the data, and why is it necessary to include that process in the formula?

Don't forget old exam papers as preparation. However, remember that reading them is not enough—you need to work through the questions to benefit from them. Again, you can sit a practice exam, and then use the paper to identify areas in which you need to do more study.

WARNING! All courses change with time. Material gets added, or chopped out. Sections of courses get swapped from one semester to another. You should check with your tutor (or your course outline and objectives) to make sure that the old exam questions you are looking at are still relevant to your course.

SHORT ANSWER AND ESSAY EXAMS

There are often short answer elements in both multiple choice and problem solving exams. Essay exams are less common, but you will occasionally be asked to write explanatory essays about theories you have studied.

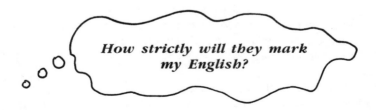

How strictly will they mark my English?

Many science students are out of practice with writing. It seems a long time since school, and most of their work at university has been scribbling numbers on tute sheets or writing a few words in blank spaces in the prac report form. If they have written anything at all, they have usually had access to a word processor with a spelling checker. Then they are suddenly faced with hand-writing cohesive paragraphs in an exam!

Good performance depends on clear communication. There are two important aspects to writing in an exam—clarity of expression, and legibility. To prepare for these tasks, it is essential for you to practise what you are going to perform. Do some writing by hand as often as you can. This is in addition to taking notes, writing lists to remember and so on. Your writing aim should be focused to express a concept clearly. Practice writing in sentences and paragraphs.

For example, you could—and should—practise writing summaries and outlines after you have revised your lecture notes or read a text. Try writing these without looking at the source! If you have taken point-form notes, test yourself to see whether you can expand these into paragraphs.

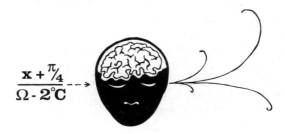

In addition to being clear, you need to be able to write quickly. There's no point in being able to present a polished paragraph in two hours if you will only have ten minutes in the exam. So keep time in mind as you work on your writing skills.

One way to do this is to time the writing that you do. You will probably be surprised how fast fifteen minutes can go when you are faced with a blank sheet of paper and a set task, without the support of your notes. You will have to write quickly in the exam, and you will become better at this the more you practise.

Analyse old exam papers if you have access to them. See if you can work out what the examiners were looking for. The course outline will also give you clues. Sometimes students become so involved with the detail of each lecture that they neglect the overall concepts of the course. Try to identify the main point or question.

Remember that in the exam you won't have as much time as you want. Try to write straight into the main points of the concept, and don't stress too much about writing fancy introductory sentences or repeating the question. Time is not money in exams—time is marks!

PRACTICAL EXAMS

At certain stages during your career as a science student you will be expected to demonstrate that you have become capable in the techniques and methodologies associated with your discipline. You will therefore often have a portion of your marks for the subject allocated for a practical exam. Usually this is a minor part, but it is one area where it is comparatively easy to obtain full marks.

To prepare for practical exams, you must practise! This sounds self-evident, but many students think that they can excel in the pracs by learning a list of what to do. That is not nearly so effective as actually practising the items on the list.

Practise, practise, practise!

As we explained earlier (in Chapter 4), physical practice as an active learning technique is effective because it involves more of our senses than passive learning. Therefore, doing practical work will help your grasp of the theory.

Don't forget, if you aren't able to get to the facilities as often as you'd like, there are still active tasks you can complete. Go through the motions in one of the ways described on page 39.

WARNING! There is a greater element of plagiarism in practical work than anywhere else. This includes copying from another student or from a past year's student (possibly at a price). In these days of large classes and heavy demonstrator workloads you may get away with this for a while. But when the practical examinations come around, the consequences can be horrible. Do your own work.

REVISION OF MEMORY PRINCIPLES

Here's an opportunity to revise some of the ideas we talked about earlier, and to apply them specifically to exam preparation. You might like to make your own list or table of techniques.

You will feel (like most science students, especially in early years) that you want to learn great chunks of information by rote. This can be useful for lists, for items in order, for some formulae, for some vocabulary, and for some structural models. For rote learning, you can use mnemonics, melodies, the method of loci, multiple repetition, peg words—and whatever else works for you. Remember that visual memory is the strongest, especially a 3-D image, and that rote learning needs constant revision.

That will work for some of your exam preparation. The bulk of it, however, will require understanding of concepts. You need this for systems, for some tabulated material, for argumentative or controversial issues, and for explaining theoretical models. Here's a recap of the principles for remembering through understanding:

- we remember what we want to remember;
- we remember what we are familiar with;
- we remember what we agree with;
- we remember what we can explain to others;
- we remember more when we have more associations;
- we remember material we can fit into patterns;
- we remember better what we have been active with.

So stay motivated; look for the meaning; organise the material; visualise the material; make associations; become very familiar with the information.

Start early in your exam preparation. It's the best advice of all.

11

SITTING YOUR EXAMS

Most of what you need to know about sitting exams successfully has been covered in the previous chapters. The importance of early preparation, of steady work throughout the teaching period, cannot be overstated. Do it early, do it often.

This chapter has a few handy hints on what to do on the day of the exam. You have probably already sat many exams quite successfully to reach university, and you can use those skills or adapt them.

However, you may not have sat such long exams and for such a large proportion of your overall mark. This may add to your anxiety about the exams. Try to be calm in your approach. The following suggestions will help you handle the whole experience better.

GENERAL EXAM ADVICE

Don't neglect your general health during the lead-up to exam period. A physically fatigued body will drain your energies so that you won't be mentally alert either. Preparing for exams is like preparing for marathons—mind and body need to work together to complete the course. Of course you already know as much as you're going to know about this subject by now, so there's no need for all-night swotting.

The night before the exam, include some relaxation activity. Physical activity can help relax your mind, which will allow it to bypass the anxiety and get at all that stored knowledge. So consider taking the family dog for a long walk or doing some yoga, or having a hit with a bat and ball in the driveway. Don't just crash in front of the television—that will provide no physical release and will allow your mind to worry.

ON E-DAY

Double-check the exam venue *personally* so there will be no confusion. You should have prepared for the journey and location well before: you know where the exam is held, how you're going to get there, and how long the trip will take. Arrive in good time on the day—not so early that you stand around with friends getting cold or hot and making each other more nervous, and not so late that you're rushing to find your seat when the others are well into reading time.

Good timing is important in other ways. During swot vac you should have been trying to make your routine suit the exam timetable as much as you can. In addition to timing yourself as you work, and doing practice exams in the set time, you can attune your mental rhythms. Are any of your exams scheduled for 3:00 a.m.? Then why are you accustoming your brain to be doing its best, most active work then? Get yourself into a routine where you are mentally active at the usual morning and afternoon sessions.

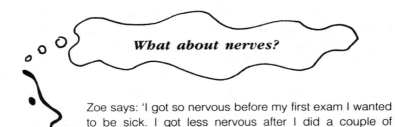

What about nerves?

Zoe says: 'I got so nervous before my first exam I wanted to be sick. I got less nervous after I did a couple of exams and they were okay, but I'm sure my results would have been better if I hadn't been so panicked. Is there anything I can do?'

Most of us suffer from exam nerves: for some people, the nerves actually improve performance, while for a few unlucky others, nerves have a terrible effect. Here are some ideas for combatting the butterflies:

- Knowing your work well is the best cure for nerves. The more confident you are about knowing the answers, the less you will be inclined to panic.
- Do lots of exam practice in exam-like conditions. Get a friend or family member to act as the exam supervisor, making you keep to time, and so on.
- If possible, get familiar with the place you will take your exam, so it is less scary.
- Try meditation or visualisation techniques to help you find your 'calm centre'.
- Practise breathing deeply to help you focus, and to fight the butterflies.
- Remind yourself that your examiners are not out to get you—in the best cases, exams are opportunities for you to show what you know.

SOME PRACTICAL CONSIDERATIONS

Make sure you have everything you need in the way of pens, pencils, calculators and so on. Those of you who have been practising aromatherapy will have drops of their favourite focusing oils on their wrists or hankies. If it's a long exam on a cold day, take some barley sugar or chocolate to keep your energy up.

A couple of technical notes. These are small points, but anything that prevents you from wasting time and getting flustered is important. Don't use white-out in an exam—it takes too long to dry. Just draw a line through what you want to erase and keep going. A healthy supply of sharpened pencils is more time-efficient than sharpening the same one throughout the exam. Choose B-type pencils rather than a very hard H—these can be difficult for examiners to read.

READING TIME

Read the paper carefully, especially the instructions. Even very bright students sometimes mess up their exams because they answer all the questions instead of just the three they were supposed to, or they miss a section.

> Sam says: 'I don't really see the point of reading time. What are you supposed to do in it? I need to be able to write to get my thoughts focused, so if I can't use a pen for the first fifteen minutes I just sit and stare at the paper.'

Reading time can be a problem, especially for those of us who suffer from nerves and need physical activity to calm down. However, that fifteen minutes is too precious to waste. You can make good use of reading time. Often, you are allowed to mark the question paper during this time; so you can write plans and outlines, decide which questions to do, and underline important words. Be on the lookout for hints and tips, and questions that appear to be related to one another.

If you aren't allowed to write, your thumb or fingernail

can be an important tool. Use your nail to underline the correct answers in a multiple choice exam; underline those important words, and mark the questions you want to do.

Other important activities for reading time include:

- reading all instructions;
- choosing questions in an essay exam;
- working out what to start with;
- locating information and quotes in an open book exam.

STARTING TO WRITE

Try to collect your thoughts a little before you put pen to paper. Stay focused, make sure you know the response format, take a deep breath, and do a relaxation routine such as isometrics. Then go to it!

Make sure you know what the questions ask, and not what you want them to ask. If you have to choose between questions, decide quickly so that you can concentrate on the chosen topics.

Some students like to begin with the easiest one first, which helps them get going. Others like to work methodically through the paper in the sequence it is presented. Both strategies are successful if you keep in mind your time limit for each question.

Stick to your time plan. You need to make frequent checks on the time, because exams are by their very essence timed assays of your ability or knowledge. Remember that you can translate the paper into so many marks per minute (or so many minutes per mark) to give you a guide for how much time to spend on each question. It's easier to get the first half of the marks for any question than to get the latter half. This means that you'll probably get more marks in total if you attempt two questions instead of spending all of that time on one question.

DOUBLE-CHECKING

You should make regular checks not only of the time, but of your calculations. In addition, it's wise to look for little things that wouldn't normally be a problem, because exam stress does funny things. Have you answered all the questions? Have you turned over two pages at once? Is your name on the paper?

Use all the time that is allowed you. Never leave an exam early—you're bound to remember something useful as soon as you leave the room, and then it's too late. Finishing extra early is a warning signal. Maybe you are brilliant, but it is more likely that you missed something.

Are there any special tricks?

MYTHS AND LEGENDS OF MULTIPLE CHOICE EXAMS

There is almost a cult growing around multiple choice exams. Rumours and 'truths' circulate just before exam time and add to the general stress. For example, you will probably hear that it is bad to change an answer because your first instinct is bound to be right. Or you may hear that it is always good to change an answer because your brain has no doubt used the intervening time to process the material properly. Which is true?

The answer is that you need to look for the best choice in every case. The exact answer you have learned may not be there. So your strategy is not to get confused and change or not change your answer because you think it's not exactly right: look for the closest appropriate response.

Keep your eyes open. It may be important to pay attention to the information in each question, rather than forgetting it as soon as you choose an answer. Sometimes lecturers put clues to the answer of a later question in a set of multiple choice answers. In addition, some questions may be cumulative, or interlinked in some way.

Another saying is that 'the answer is usually *c*'. Of course, this may happen, but many exams have their alternatives sequenced randomly, so there is no guarantee that *c* is the examiner's favourite. A similar belief is that *d* is always a filler and therefore never right; for the same reason, treat this advice cautiously.

If the stem of a question looks completely unfamiliar, try putting the ideas into everyday terms. Sometimes it is the wording, not the concepts, that has you confused. Read all the alternatives rather than leaping onto what looks like the obvious answer. Watch out for qualifying words (such as 'always', 'almost', 'never') which can alter the meaning of the sentence; and remember to look for the 'best' answer (which may not be exactly the same as the one in your notes).

PROBLEM SOLVING EXAMS

You already know the general rules for these. Write down the formulae you will need for each question, and note what you have been told and what you need to work out. If you can, it's a good idea to make a rough estimate of the order of your answer so that you can tell whether or not you're close.

Other strategies are to draw a diagram of the process to help you see what is missing and what you need to supply. If you can't immediately see how to tackle the problem, DON'T PANIC! Use a relaxation strategy such as counting to ten, visualise yourself doing a similar problem during the year, mentally review those collaborative problem solving sessions, or try another question and come back to that one later.

Again, reviewing your answers is important. Check your workings as you go, and try to make time at the end of the exam for another check. This will allow you to change your mental perspective and perhaps pick up any careless errors.

SHORT ANSWER OR ESSAY EXAMS

Be aware of the weighting for each of these questions, and allocate your time accordingly. Of course, you will read the question carefully before you start writing, but you should also refer back to it during your writing, otherwise you might go off track.

Balance your time budget. Use all the time you have for each question, even if you leave the question and return to it later. You can't earn more marks for any question than have been allocated by the examiner, so don't think you can spend more time on something you know really well and fudge the rest. It won't work!

Do I need an outline?

Using a point-form plan can help you organise your ideas. In addition, sketching a quick plan on your first page can also help to squeeze an extra mark or two. If you don't finish, but your examiner can see where you were heading, he/she might give you the benefit of the doubt.

Although using a plan will help you to order your response, you should also leave some space for revision. Try to write on every second line, or leave some space between paragraphs (it's okay to ask for a second or third answer booklet). That way, if you re-read the essay and need to put in more information, you can. As a last resort, number your paragraphs and put the extra points at the end, with an indication of where they belong in the body of your essay.

As long as you clearly indicate the number of the question, it's not necessary to repeat the question or even some of the words; in an exam you can jump straight in to the essentials of the answer.

Make every sentence and every point worth marks. Imagine the examiner: will she put a tick next to that sentence? Or will she know it was a waffly bit of filling because you are a bit vague about the topic? Don't waste words, be concise.

Although it's not useful to have a full-blown introduction in a short answer question (for a longish essay answer—40 minutes to an hour—you can use the niceties more), it is always essential to conclude with a really relevant point. This will remind the marker that you know what you're talking about. Don't finish with a lame, vague sentence that could be used for any topic. Make sure you leave the reader with an impression of your ability to expound at length on the topic.

PRACTICAL EXAMS

There are different types of practical exams. These are often conducted during teaching time rather than in the true examination period. Sometimes they consist of an overall mark for your performance in practicals throughout the year, in which case you need to make sure you attend every prac and pay good attention.

At other times you will be asked individually or in small groups to show what you know about methodology, or you will be presented with 'fresh' results and asked to analyse them on the spot. When this happens, you may find that you become very nervous before and during the assessment.

The general rules about exams are applicable here as well. You can employ some of those relaxation exercises at appropriate times, and you can try the sports psychology approach of mentally convincing yourself that you can do it, and visualising yourself succeeding at the task.

However, in practical exams there is no substitute for familiarity with the routine. Frequent practice is your best preparation, either in the actual or in pretend situations, so that you are confident enough to perform well in front of examiners. It's like going for your driver's licence: you may be nervous on the day but if you really know what you're about, it will be obvious to the examiner despite a couple of shaky starts.

This is one place where it is extremely counter-productive to gather with a group of friends beforehand, talking hysterically about how scared you are. You will only raise your own and everyone else's anxiety levels. Do something positive instead, like taking a brisk walk around campus to work off some of that nervous energy.

AFTER THE EXAM

Don't agonise over it! You can't change anything now, and relating how horrible it was may make you feel worse instead of better, and deflect you from your next chore—you probably have another exam in a day or so, and you need to marshal all your mental and physical energies for that.

(Of course you can celebrate the relief when everything is finished.) Let the exam go.

One exception to this advice is if you were feeling sick or had some other problem on the exam day. If you did, it's important to let your marker know. Apply for special consideration straight away—it'll be too late if you wait.

UNPLEASANT SURPRISES

Joel says: 'During swot vac I studied really well for my Biology exam. I used old papers to practise all the types of questions—multiple choice, problems and short answers. I thought I was really prepared. Then I got in to the exam, and the first question was an essay. I was really thrown, none of the previous exams had essays, and we weren't told we would have to do one. I think I did okay, because I can write essays, but I would have done better if I'd *known* it would happen.'

Sometimes, exams are just awful—everyone finds them difficult, and you come out feeling like a wet rag. If you've prepared well, and answered to the best of your ability, all you can do is hope for the best. You should be fine. You can also console yourself with the thought that people who are confident about their performance may be disappointed by their results: if you're sure you've bombed, you might be pleasantly surprised.

Don't believe everything you hear, and don't worry too much.

Remember that students are just as notoriously unrealistic about telling each other how they went in the exam as they are at saying how much time they spend studying. If your friend is in tears and bemoaning her efforts, you don't feel you can say that you were happy with the questions, so you agree. Lots of exam post mortems are extremely unrealistic. Just show appropriate sympathy and get on with your next event.

WHAT TO DO WHEN THINGS GO WRONG

Tertiary study is about becoming an adult. When you encounter problems, it is your responsibility to do something about them. There is a wide variety of help available at most campuses for all sorts of situations (health, finance, study problems . . .), but these people won't come to you. You need to identify what has gone wrong and look for solutions. In this chapter we'll outline some common study problems and give you starting points for dealing with them.

> Joel says: 'I found it hard to get into the swing of uni life. I always used to be able to ask my parents for help when I was at school, but my dad never went to uni, and my mum went to uni in Poland, so they didn't really have much idea about my problems. I had to look in my diary to find out the stuff I needed to know. I got a lot of help from the "contact" people at the student union—once I actually walked into their office.'

I don't like my demonstrator and she doesn't like me.

One thing that it's good to realise is that most demonstrators and tutors are postgraduate students who do some teaching as part of their research duties or to earn a little extra money. Unlike your school teachers, these people have not dedicated their lives to teaching, and they often have very little experience. However, they do have a good knowledge of their subject and recent experience of being a university student, and they can share these with you. So perhaps you need to give your demonstrator a chance.

Take *positive* action. If the personality clash is causing real difficulties, you can try asking to change tutes, or you can wait a bit and see whether demonstrators change with the topics you are studying. You could also look on it as character building, remembering that you won't always get to work with people you like. If the person is really hopeless, go and see the lecturer or first year coordinator (phrasing your complaints in a polite and rational manner). You are now responsible for your own progress, and you should take action about problems that are affecting your learning and results.

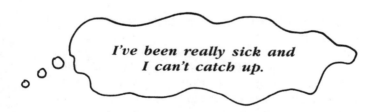

Student lifestyles seem to be conducive to the flu. The best solution is to make sure you pay attention to your diet, exercise and sleep. Although study is mainly a mental activity, you need a healthy body to let your mind work at its most efficient.

If you have been sick and had to miss classes, you can try some of these strategies:

- Don't get further behind—do *this* week's work before you think about revising all the bits you missed.
- Do your catching up backwards—don't worry if you don't understand it all. You can fill in the gaps later and just take it on trust until all the pieces fit together.
- Talk to someone about what you missed—half an hour's chat can be more useful than trying to decipher someone else's notes.
- If you're not feeling really well, don't force yourself to endlessly re-read long boring chapters. Do a little active work, small bits at a time.

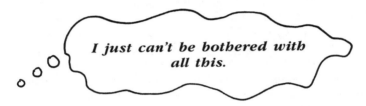

I just can't be bothered with all this.

It is not unusual to feel bored and lose motivation at some stage during your studies. Everybody gets bored with study and with putting the rest of their lives on hold while they complete their degree. For some people, a walk on the beach or a chocolate sundae will cure the problem, but for others it is not quite that easy to get fired up again.

We've talked a lot about study habits in earlier chapters. Many of these strategies can actually help to improve your motivation if you use them on a regular basis. So if you're feeling dull and listless about your study, why not try some of the following (you can find more detail in earlier chapters):

- set some clear short-term goals;
- set yourself a time-frame;
- reward yourself for completing tasks;
- break your tasks into bite-sized pieces;
- stop procrastinating—deal with the hard bits first;

- refocus on the long view;
- do some study with some friends;
- don't make excuses—make progress.

But sometimes it is boring!

We know. Don't fight it. In some courses, you're required to take subjects that would never otherwise have been on your list of possibles. There must be a very good reason for this! If you're not clear how this subject can benefit you, ask the teaching staff. You can also treat it as something rather uninteresting that just needs to be done—like brushing your teeth. Changing your toothpaste might make it more stimulating for a while—what about making something special for the hated subject? Using a special coloured pen or paper, or rewarding yourself with a marshmallow cocoa every time you complete a tute sheet?

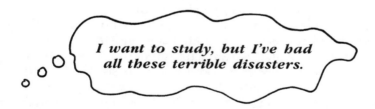

I want to study, but I've had all these terrible disasters.

Disasters come in all shapes and sizes. Try to put your problems in perspective—yes, it's awful to have the 'flu three times in one winter, but is that the same as being in hospital and rehab for six months? You need to tailor your reactions to the severity of the problem. Of course it seems bad to you, but how will other people view it?

This is not to say that you won't get sympathy and support, but if you drop out of subjects every time something bad happens, you'll never finish your course. Don't make any hasty decisions without advice from people such as those we mentioned above, and remember that there is specific help available for many of the crises that occur in everyone's life. It may be that you need to drop some subjects, or go part time, or take a year off, but these are last resorts.

You'll find that all the active study strategies suggested in this book will make your study time more efficient, so even if you are having other problems in your life, you can still continue with your course. If you're feeling too upset to study, try to recognise that all the qualities that made you a good student in the past still belong to you, and that you can access them. Don't let the feeling overwhelm you, but acknowledge that it's part of your life at the moment. You may find it helpful to make a list of strategies for yourself that you know have been valuable in the past. Concentrate on small achievable goals and reward yourself for reaching them.

It's swot vac and I haven't started studying.

Leaving everything until too late can be a problem, especially in early years. The university year goes by very quickly. If you know you're in trouble, you can do something about it. If there were serious reasons which prevented you from studying earlier in the year, you must identify and follow up the procedures for special consideration. Most universities (and most faculties) have people who can help you with these sorts of problems. They may be called course advisers, mentors, peer tutors, learning skills advisers, counsellors, or some other title. As a first step, get in touch with these people and ask for help.

Don't waste your precious time by spending hours mentally berating yourself for all the things you haven't done. What is important now is to maximise your return from the limited time you have. You can still make use of all the active learning strategies we talked of earlier; you just have to do them in a more concentrated way.

Here are some other things you can do:

- Make a study timetable for the remaining time so you know that you can cover all you need to cover.
- Focus on the level of knowledge you need to get through each subject—this is no time to indulge your perfectionism.
- 'Slash and burn': if there are things that you know you're never going to understand, don't waste time on them.
- Concentrate on improving your knowledge in areas where you've got a good basic grasp of what is happening (full marks on half the questions is a better return than 30 per cent on everything).
- Don't stay up all night—the extra pages read overnight aren't worth the decrease in performance next day.

Sam says: 'My brother and his friends at Sydney Uni say that if you haven't started studying by the time the jacaranda is in flower, you are in big trouble.' (Of course, that's a locally specific guide. It won't help you if you live in a cooler climate!)

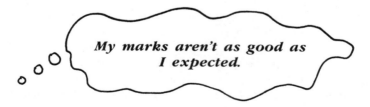

My marks aren't as good as I expected.

These things happen. It is disappointing; the only thing to do is vow to learn from your mistakes. As a consolation, remember you are now studying at a higher level than you have done in the past. You are also surrounded by lots of similarly brainy students, so you may find it a bit of a shock to be getting average marks when you're used to being top of the class.

That said, you can probably do better if you adjust your approach and study techniques to match the task more closely. Ask yourself some hard questions and answer them honestly:

- Are you doing regular study every day?
- Are you reviewing frequently?
- Are you allowing adequate time for preparation?
- Are you studying actively (as opposed to doing 'desk time')?
- Are you making your study a priority?

If you are saying 'yes' to all of these, but you're still not achieving as well as you wish, then there are a couple of things to consider. First, if you persist, you will soon begin to consolidate your efforts. Another factor to consider is your motivation—are you in the right course? Maybe you're having problems because you're just not as interested in your subjects as you thought you would be.

Everyone expected me to do well.

This can be really hard, but the bottom line is that it's your life and it's up to you to decide your priorities. Some students find themselves in courses that don't really suit them. You may have chosen your course because of some family pressure, or because of a course description that doesn't match the reality of the daily grind. It may be that you're just finding out about how to function successfully at uni; it may be that you had other issues to deal with; it may be that the other people don't understand exactly how hard study at this level is.

You have options about these pressures. You can try explaining to your family or friends what the situation really is. You can ask them to help you re-evaluate your goals. You can talk to someone who is totally neutral. If things are really bad, you may want to move out of home to try to establish yourself as an independent adult. If you really feel that you should live up to other people's expectations and you haven't been able to do so, try seeking extra help (from a learning skills adviser, or maybe you could hire a private tutor) to ensure better results in the next semester.

Um, I failed.

You may not believe this now, but it's not the end of the world as we know it. It's not even necessarily the end of your course, or even that subject. Many successful graduates failed their first assignment; mostly that's because they were adjusting to university. If you know you could have worked harder, then the solution to your problem is fairly clear. The time to worry is when it was totally unexpected, and you can't see what to improve.

Know where you stand. Even if you know deep down that you didn't put anywhere near enough study into the subject, it's still beneficial to look at your exam paper or ask for detailed feedback on your written assignments. It may be that you were not as hopeless as you believed—there are bound to be positive aspects to any assessment. Perhaps you just had a bad day for simple addition; perhaps you misread the assignment topic but your work was otherwise sound. Just as it's important to know what you don't know, it's also useful to see how much you've absorbed.

> Zoe says: 'I had a terrible experience because I was so nervous in my first exams. I studied a couple of topics in Maths in a lot of detail, but there weren't any questions on them in the exam. Or so I thought. When I was talking to people afterwards, I realised I must have missed a whole page, and they were questions I could have answered.'

THE BOTTOM LINE

The main message is that nobody's study life is perfect. You can't plan for accidents, but if you make an effort to keep up throughout the year, then you will minimise the damage.

CONCLUSION

ENJOY YOUR YEAR

Your first year of university experience is unique, and no-one can really tell you exactly what it will be like for you. It's important to listen to all the advice and guidance that is available, but ultimately you need to decide what suits you. Along the way you will also discover a lot about yourself and how you do things. Your first year is as much about learning how to do things at university as it is about understanding subject content.

So how did Zoe, Joel and Sam go in their first year?

Zoe got good results in all her subjects. She passed everything and got honours in Chemistry. Her marks weren't as good as she hoped, and she didn't get into Veterinary Science. However, she has discovered that she really likes Chem, especially lab work. So her goals for her university course have changed a bit; next year she is going to do more Chem subjects and is thinking about becoming an industrial chemist.

Sam had a really good time in college. He was in the rowing team, in the musical, and made heaps of friends. Social life was Sam's priority in his first year, and his marks reflected this. He passed most of his subjects (one with a supp) and failed Maths in second semester. He still doesn't really know what he wants to do—except that he doesn't want to do Maths anymore! His parents are really concerned about his results. Next year Sam wants to move into a house with some friends, but his parents think he should move home so that he has a better study environment.

Joel got excellent marks in Sociology and Biology. Those are the subjects he's going to concentrate on in second year. He passed his other subjects but he didn't like them very much. Because he's doing a combined course, he has lots of flexibility. Next year he's going to pick up some new subjects including Beginners' Japanese. It took him a while to settle in at uni but he went hiking with the Mountaineering Club at Easter and he now has some friends to talk to at uni.

These students all had different experiences of first year, which shows that there's more to first year than simply studying. They have all grown and learned in many ways—some have changed their goals or made new decisions and discoveries about themselves. They are all wiser about university life, and feel that they know a lot more than the new first years just arriving.

In this book, we have outlined a number of the issues that face students approaching university for the first time. Remember, many universities regard first year as a trial and orientation period. During this year both you and your university need to get used to one another. Establishing good study habits now will put you in a good position to succeed in your course.

Studying science can lead to all sorts of fun and exciting careers and activities. University at its best will challenge and excite your intellect, and show you lots of possibilities to explore. If you are looking for some inspiration about the fabulous things scientists do, check out what scientists are up to on the web. 'The Annals of Improbable Research' <http://www.improb.com/> might give you a few ideas.

APPENDIX I

SUGGESTIONS FOR
FURTHER READING

AGPS (Australian Government Printing Service). 1995. Style Manual for Authors and Printers. 5th edition. AGPS, Canberra

This has clear and helpful guidelines on referencing as well as useful guidelines for using abbreviations, numbers, figures and so on. A good reference book that you can use throughout your study career, and as a professional.

Day, R.A. 1991. How to Write and Publish a Scientific Paper. 3rd edition. Cambridge University Press, Cambridge.

Examples of types of scientific papers, clear guidelines for illustrations, a list of scientific abbreviations, and strategies for writing good scientific English.

Gawith, G. 1991. Power Learning: A Student's Guide to Success. Longman Cheshire, Melbourne

Useful discussion of learning styles, time management strategies, and study planning. Later chapters more applicable to arts students.

Murray-Smith, S. 1989. 2nd edition. Right Words: A Guide to English Usage in Australia. Penguin, Ringwood, Victoria, Australia

Contains lots of good advice about pronunciation, spelling, grammar and usage.

Pechenik, J.A. 1993. A Short Guide to Writing about Biology. HarperCollins College Publishers, New York

A useful guide for writing biology lab reports and essays, with many examples.

Porush, D. 1995. A Short Guide to Writing about Science. HarperCollins College Publishers, New York

A useful guide to the general types of writing in science, with guidelines about citations and setting out your work.

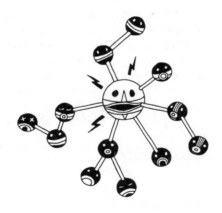

APPENDIX II

LEARNING STYLES QUIZ

For each of the following statements, rate yourself in order to discover your strengths and weaknesses. You probably will find that although you use strategies from all sections at some time or other, there will be one or two that stand out as your preferred learning modes. If things are spread pretty evenly, then maybe you are a well-balanced learner!

LEARNING STYLES

	Always	Sometimes	Never
Visuo-spatial			
I like to have my room organised so that all the things that go together stay together.	☐	☐	☐
I like to draw a map if someone is giving me directions.	☐	☐	☐
I like to make poster-style charts to study from.	☐	☐	☐
I use my hands or a drawing to help me describe complex things to other people.	☐	☐	☐

	Always	Sometimes	Never
When I try to remember things, I can picture the page or the place I first saw them.	☐	☐	☐

Visuo-verbal

	Always	Sometimes	Never
I like to read over the instructions before I try something new.	☐	☐	☐
I like to rewrite things I have to learn.	☐	☐	☐
I like to make lists of things to do.	☐	☐	☐
I use lots of describing words when I'm explaining things to people.	☐	☐	☐
I like to take notes in complete sentences.	☐	☐	☐

Auditory

	Always	Sometimes	Never
I like to repeat instructions as I do new tasks.	☐	☐	☐
I prefer to listen to a story than to read the book.	☐	☐	☐
I like to talk over the lessons with some of my friends.	☐	☐	☐
I like people asking me questions so I can talk about what I've done or learned.	☐	☐	☐
I take point-form notes and don't like writing essays.	☐	☐	☐

Kinaesthetic

	Always	Sometimes	Never
I like to try something without bothering about the written instructions.	☐	☐	☐
I love taking things apart to see how they work.	☐	☐	☐

	Always	Sometimes	Never
I like to make patterns of the things I have to learn.	☐	☐	☐
I'm good at practical tasks if people don't pester me.	☐	☐	☐
When I explain something, I use anything around me—knives and forks and sauce bottles—to show how the parts fit together.	☐	☐	☐

There is no 'right' or 'wrong' way to learn. You can use any mode to learn, but what you should consider is that some modes suit some types of learning better. For example, if you are studying for a practical exam, you should use some kinaesthetic methods: try doing the procedure without following written instructions; make sure you know how the parts fit together.

LEARNING TEMPERAMENTS

This little quiz is to help you identify your individual learning temperament. Once again, there are no right or wrong answers, and some sorts of information are more easily learned by those with one temperament or another. The best teachers enable students to approach the material from a multitude of directions; at tertiary level, you may need to organise this for yourself.

	Always	Sometimes	Never
The big picture learner			
Once I get an overview, the details fall into place.	☐	☐	☐

	Always	Sometimes	Never
I like to get a feel for how the information fits together.	☐	☐	☐
I like to know what I'm meant to get out of a task before I start it.	☐	☐	☐
I like to look at the last page before I go back and read the rest of the book.	☐	☐	☐

The step-by-step learner

	Always	Sometimes	Never
I want to get each section right before I move on.	☐	☐	☐
I'm uncomfortable when new things happen really quickly.	☐	☐	☐
If I concentrate on the details and examples, I will work out the theory later.	☐	☐	☐
I like to see every episode of a TV series in order.	☐	☐	☐

The experiential learner

	Always	Sometimes	Never
I like to try out things for myself and test theories for myself.	☐	☐	☐
I tend to argue with people about how things work because I see them in my own way.	☐	☐	☐
I sometimes find that I discover things by myself.	☐	☐	☐
When I get a new computer game, I don't read the instructions, I just play and work it out as I go along.	☐	☐	☐

The collaborative learner

	Always	Sometimes	Never
I like talking over the lessons because other people can show me a different side of the information.	☐	☐	☐

	Always	Sometimes	Never
I find that describing things to other people helps me to understand them myself.	☐	☐	☐
If I don't understand something, I'd rather ask someone about it than read a book.	☐	☐	☐
I can work quite well in a noisy environment.	☐	☐	☐

These short questionnaires are just starting points. If you are interested to find out more about yourself and your learning style, there are lots of online resources. Some of them even have long quizzes that you can do. A good starting place is 'The Keirsey Temperament Sorter <http://sunsite.unc.edu/personality/keirsey.html> or at <http://www.keirsey.com>. This page presents an online personality test you can do, and it gives detailed feedback about each personality type.

APPENDIX III

A STARTING POINT FOR USING WEB RESOURCES

FUN (AND INFORMATIVE) SCIENCE SITES

The Annals of Improbable Research
<http://www.improb.com/>

The Mad Scientist Network
<http://medinfo.wustl.edu/~ysp/MSN/>

Science Hobbyist
<http://www.eskimo.com/~billb/index.html>

Geek Site of the Day
<http://www.owlnet.rice.edu/~indigo/gsotd/>

All of the above sites have links to online research projects. Here are a couple more:

VolcanoWorld
<http://volcano.und.nodak.edu/>

Bunny Survival Tests Homepage
<http://www.pcola.gulf.net/~irving/bunnies/>

SCIENCE JOURNALS ONLINE

Science Online
<http://science-mag.aaas.org/>

Nature
<http://www.nature.com/>

New Scientist Planet Science
<http://www.newscientist.co.uk/>

Scientific American
<http://www.sciam.com/>

Something to aspire to:

Nobel Prizes Internet Archive
<http://nobelprizes.com/>

PERSONALITY AND LEARNING STYLES INFORMATION AND TESTS

Two good places to start are the page of IQ and personality tests on the web:
<http://www.2h.com/welcome.phtml>

or you can try Yahoo! for some links:
<http://www.yahoo.com/Science/Psychology/>

ONLINE HELP WITH WRITING AND STUDY

The Learning Skills Unit at the University of Melbourne
<http://www.services.unimelb.edu.au/lsu/>

The Learning Development Centre at the University of Western Sydney (Macarthur)
<http://www.macarthur.uws.edu.au/ssd/ldc/Resources.html>

Mind Tools—Memory Techniques and Mnemonics
<http://www.bazis.nl/personal/vermey/memory.html>

ONLINE CITATION GUIDELINES

A good starting web site for referencing guidelines is:
<http://www.ddce.cqu.edu.au/refandcitation/home.htm>

A site with a lot more detail and links to other resources:

Louisiana State University 'How to Cite the Internet'
<http://www.lsu.edu/guests/poli/public_html/lis.html>

A specific guide for students required to use the APA style:
<http://www.beadsland.com/weapas/>